Professional Pilot's Study Guide Volume 4

Electrics

Mike Burton

Airlife
England

Copyright © 1991 Mike Burton

First published in the UK in 1992
by Airlife Publishing Ltd

British Library Cataloguing in Publication Data
A catalogue record of this book is available from the British Library

ISBN 1 85310 276 8

Printed in England by Livesey Ltd, Shrewsbury SY3 9EB

Airlife Publishing Ltd
101 Longden Road, Shrewsbury SY3 9EB

Contents

1

THE ELECTRON

1.1 Introduction

Anyone concerned with aviation is aware of the increasing use of electricity in modern aircraft systems and recognizes the importance of a thorough understanding of electrical principles.

In the study of physics, the electron theory of the structure of matter explains the fundamental nature of matter. A more detailed examination of this theory is necessary to explain the behaviour of the electron as it applies to the study of basic electricity.

1.2 Matter

Matter can be defined as anything that has mass (weight) and occupies space. Thus, matter is everything that exists. It may exist in the form of solids, liquids, or gases. The smallest particle of matter in any state or form, that still possesses its identity, is called a molecule.

Substances composed of only one type of atom are called elements. But most substances occur in nature as compounds, that is, combinations of two or more types of atoms. Water, for example, is a compound of two atoms of hydrogen and one atom of oxygen. A molecule of water is illustrated in Figure 1. It would no longer retain the characteristics of water if it was compounded of one atom of hydrogen and two atoms of oxygen.

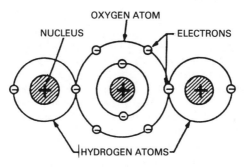

Fig.1-1. A water molecule.

1.3 The Atom

The atom is considered the basic building block of all matter. It is the smallest possible particle that an element can be divided into and still retain its chemical properties. In its simplest form, it consists of one or

1

more electrons orbiting at a high rate of speed around a centre, or nucleus, made up of one or more protons, and, in most atoms, one or more neutrons as well. Since an atom is so small that some 200,000 could be placed side by side in a line 1 inch long, it cannot be seen, of course. Nevertheless, a great deal is known about its behaviour from various tests and experiments.

The simplest atom is that of hydrogen, which is one electron orbiting around one proton, as shown in Figure 2. A more complex atom is that of oxygen (see Figure 3), which consists of eight electrons rotating in two different orbits around a nucleus made up of eight protons and eight neutrons.

An electron is the basic negative charge of electricity and cannot be divided further. Some electrons are more tightly bound to the nucleus of their atom than others and rotate in an imaginary shell or sphere close to the nucleus, while others are more loosely bound and orbit at a greater distance from the nucleus. These latter electrons are called 'free' electrons because they can be freed easily from the positive attraction of the protons in the nucleus to make up the flow of electrons in a practical electrical circuit.

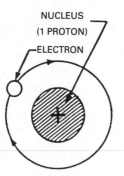

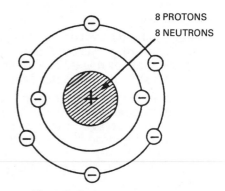

Fig.1-2. Hydrogen atom.   Fig.1-3. Oxygen atom.

The neutrons in a nucleus have no electrical charge. They are neither positive nor negative but are equal in size and weight to the proton. Since a proton weighs approximately 1,845 times as much as an electron, the overall weight of an atom is determined by the number of protons and neutrons in its nucleus. The weight of an electron is not considered in determining the weight of an atom. Indeed, the nature of electricity cannot be defined clearly because it is not certain whether the electron is a negative charge with no mass (weight) or a particle of matter with a negative charge.

Electricity is best understood in terms of its behaviour, which is based in part on the charge an atom carries. When the total positive charge of the protons in the nucleus equals the total negative charge of the electrons in orbit around the nucleus, the atom is said to have a neutral charge. If an atom has a shortage of electrons, or negative charges, it is positively charged and is called a positive ion. If it possesses an excess of electrons, it is said to be negatively charged and is called a negative ion.

1.4 Electron Movement

In a state of neutral charge, an atom has one electron for each proton in the nucleus. Thus, the number of electrons held by the atoms making up the various elements will vary from one, in the case of hydrogen, to 92 for uranium.

The electrons revolving around a nucleus travel in orbits, sometimes called shells or layers. Each shell can contain a certain maximum number of electrons, and if this number is exceeded, the extra electrons will be forced into the next higher, or outer, shell.

The shell nearest the nucleus can contain no more than two electrons. In an atom containing more than two electrons, the excess electrons will be located in the outer shells. The second shell can have a maximum of eight electrons. The third shell can hold up to 18 electrons, the fourth 32, etc. It should be noted, however, that in some large complex atoms electrons may be arranged in outer shells before some inner shells are filled.

1.5 Static Electricity

Electricity is often described as being either static or dynamic. Since all electrons are alike, these words do not actually describe two different types of electricity; rather, they distinguish between electrons at rest and those in motion. The word static means 'stationary' or 'at rest', and refers to the deficiency or to the excess of electrons. Originally it was thought that static electricity was electricity at rest because electrical energy produced by friction did not move. A simple experiment, such as running a dry comb through hair, will produce cracking or popping sounds, indicating static discharges are taking place. The charges thus built up consist of electrons transferred to the comb as the result of friction. The discharge is caused by the rapid movement of electrons in the opposite direction from the comb to the hair as the charges neutralise each other. In the dark it is possible to see these discharges as tiny sparks.

Static electricity has little practical value, and often causes problems. It is difficult to control and discharges quickly. Conversely, dynamic, or current electricity, is generated and controlled easily and provides energy for useful work. A summary of that part of the electron theory dealing with charges will help explain static electricity. All electrons are alike and repel each other. Similarly all protons are alike and repel each other. Electrons and protons are not alike, but attract each other. Hence, the fundamental law of electricity is that like charges repel and unlike charges attract.

1.6 Generation of Static Electricity

Static electricity can be produced by contact, friction or induction. As an example of the friction method, a glass rod rubbed with fur becomes negatively charged, but if rubbed with silk, becomes positively charged. Some materials that build up static electricity easily are flannel, silk, rayon, amber, hard rubber, and glass.

When two materials are rubbed together, some electron orbits of atoms in one material may cross the orbits or shells of the other, and one material may give up electrons to the other. The transferred electrons are those in the outer shells or orbits and are called free electrons.

The effects of static electricity must be considered in the operation and maintenance of aircraft. Static interference in the aircraft communication systems and the static charge created by the aircraft's movement through the air are examples of problems created by static electricity. Parts of the aircraft must be 'bonded' or joined together to provide a low-resistance (or easy) path for static discharge, and radio parts must be shielded. Static charges must be considered in the refuelling of the aircraft to prevent possible igniting of the fuel, and provision must be made to ground the aircraft structure, either by static-conducting tyres or by a grounding wire.

1.7   Electrostatic Field

A field of force exists around a charged body. This field is an electrostatic field (sometimes called a dielectric field) and is represented by lines extending in all directions from the charged body and terminating where there is an equal and opposite charge.

To explain the action of an electrostatic field, lines are used to represent the direction and intensity of the electric field of force. As illustrated in Figure 4, the intensity of the field is indicated by the number of lines per unit area, and the direction is shown by arrowheads on the lines pointing in the direction in which a small test charge would move or tend to move if acted upon by the field of force.

Either a positive or negative test charge can be used, but it has been arbitrarily agreed that a small positive charge will always be used in determining the direction of the field. Thus, the direction of the field around a positive charge is always away from the charge, as shown in Figure 4, because a positive test charge would be repelled. On the other hand, the direction of the lines about a negative charge is towards the charge, since a positive test charge is attracted towards it.

Figure 1-5 illustrates the field around bodies having like charges. Positive charges are shown, but regardless of the type of charge, the lines of force would repel each other if the charges were alike. The lines terminate on material objects and always extend from a positive charge to a negative charge. These lines are imaginary lines used to show the direction a real force takes.

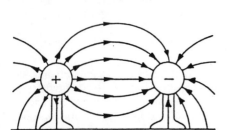

Fig.1-4. Direction of electric field around positive and negative charges.

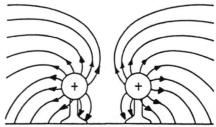

Fig.1-5. Field around two positively charged bodies.

1.8   Electromotive Force

The flow of electrons from a negative point to a positive point is called an electric current; this current flows because of a difference in electric pressure between the two points.

If an excess of electrons with a negative charge exists at one end of a conductor and a deficiency of electrons with a positive charge at the other, an electrostatic field exists between the two charges. Electrons are repelled from the negatively charged point and are attracted by the positively charged point.

The flow of electrons of electric current can be compared to the flow of water between two interconnected water tanks when a difference of pressure exists between two tanks. Figure 6 shows the level of water in tank A to be at a higher level than the water level in tank B. If the valve in the interconnecting line between the tanks is opened, water will flow from tank A into tank B until the level of water is the same in both tanks. It is important to note that it was not the pressure in tank A that caused the water to flow; rather, it was the difference in pressure between tank A and tank B that caused the flow. When the water in the two tanks is at the same level, the flow of water ceases because there is no longer a difference of pressure.

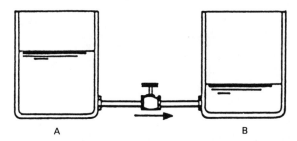

Fig. 1-6. Difference of pressure.

This comparison illustrates the principle that causes the electrons to move, when a proper path is available, from a point of excess electrons to a point deficient in electrons. The force that causes this movement is the potential difference in electrical energy between the two points. This force is called the electrical pressure or the potential difference or the electromotive force (electron-moving force) which can all be considered the same thing. Electromotive force, abbreviated e.m.f., causes current (electrons) to move in an electric path or circuit. The practical unit of measurement of e.m.f., or potential difference, is the volt. The symbol for e.m.f. is the capital 'E'.

If the water pressure in tank A of Figure 6 is 10 p.s.i. and the pressure in tank B is 2 p.s.i. there is a difference in pressure of 8 p.s.i. Similarly, it can be said that an electromotive force of 8 volts exists between two electrical points. Since potential difference is measured in volts, the word 'voltage' can also be used to describe amounts of potential difference. Thus, it is correct to say that the voltage of a certain aircraft battery is 24 volts, another means of indicating that a potential difference of 24 volts exists between two points connected by a conductor.

1.9 Current Flow

Electrons in motion make up an electric current. This electric current is usually referred to as 'current' or 'current flow', no matter how many electrons are moving. When the current flow is in one direction only, it is called direct current. Later in the study of electrical fundamentals, current that reverses itself periodically, called alternating current, will be discussed. In the present study all references are to direct current.

Since an electric current may consist of varying numbers of electrons, it is important to know the number of electrons flowing in a circuit in a given time. Electrons can be counted by measuring the basic electrical charge on each electron. Since this charge is very small, a practical unit, the coulomb, is used to measure an amount, or quantity, of electrical charge. The accumulated charge on 6.28 billion electrons is called one coulomb. When this quantity of electrons flows past a given point in an electrical circuit, one ampere of current is said to be flowing in the circuit. Current flow is measured in amperes or parts of amperes by an electrical instrument called an ammeter. The symbol used to indicate current in formulas or on schematics is the capital letter 'I', which stands for the intensity of current flow.

Fig. 1-7. Electron movement.

The drift of free electrons must not be confused with the concept of current flow that approaches the speed of light. When a voltage is applied to a circuit, the free electrons travel but a short distance before colliding with atoms. These collisions usually knock other electrons free from their atoms, and these electrons travel on towards the positive terminal of the wire, colliding with other atoms as they drift at a comparatively slow rate of speed. To understand the almost instantaneous speed of the effect of electric current, it is helpful to visualize a long tube filled with steel balls as shown in Figure 1-7.

It can be seen that a ball introduced in one end of the tube, which represents a conductor, will immediately cause a ball to be emitted at the opposite end of the tube. Even if the tube was long enough to reach clear across the country, this effect could still be visualized as being instantaneous. Thus, electric current flow can be viewed as occurring instantaneously, even though it is a result of a comparatively slow drift of electrons.

2

BASIC ELECTRICAL PRINCIPLES

2.1 Introduction

The modern conception of electricity, is based on the electron theory, a brief description of which is shown in chapter one. In accordance with this theory an electric current is defined as an orderly movement of electrons from one part of a circuit to another.

To obtain this movement of electrons in a simple circuit it is necessary to first have a source of electrical pressure such as a battery, sometimes called an accumulator, or a generator, and secondly, a complete external electrical circuit, comprising a system of electrical conductors, (wires) connected to that source of electrical pressure.

In such a circuit the flow of current is, conventionally, from the positive terminal (+) of the source of electrical pressure, through the system of conductors, to the negative (−) terminal. The actual movement of electrons, is however, in the opposite direction. Each electron, being a minute electrical charge of electricity, is always attracted to a positive charge, therefore, the electron flow is from the negative terminal to the positive terminal.

2.2 Conductors and Insulators

A conductor is a material in which electrons are only loosely attached to their groups, so that application of electrical pressure causes these free electrons to move through the material in the direction of the electromotive force, that is the source of pressure such as the battery or the generator.

In general all metals can be classed as conductors, while some non-metallic materials such as carbon and acids also conduct electricity. Some materials permit the movement of electrons more freely than others, the measure of ease with which they do is known as their conductance. For example metals such as copper and aluminium have high conductivity and are generally used for electrical conductors (wires).

Conductance is therefore the standard of comparison between different conducting materials; the reciprocal of conductance, i.e. resistance, however, is used in calculations.

Insulators, which are also known as dielectrics, are materials in which electrons are so firmly attached to their groups that little or no electron movement, or flow, takes place when electrical pressure is applied. At normal pressure such materials are considered as non-conductors. If however, the applied pressure is progressively increased a point is reached at which the material breaks down and passes current. The ability of a known thickness of insulating material to resist, or prevent, such breakdown is called its dielectric strength.

Although there is no perfect non-conductor, materials such as rubber, cotton, porcelain and bakelite are termed non-conductors or insulators; pure distilled water is also a non-conductor.

2.3   Electrical Pressure, Current, and Resistance

Three primary conditions exist in the simple electrical circuit. First the electrical pressure; secondly, the flow of electrical current; and thirdly, the degree with which materials conduct electricity.

(a) Electrical Pressure
The electrical pressure which causes an electric current to flow in a circuit is known as the electromotive force (E.M.F.). It may be produced in three ways:

(1)   By chemical action as in a primary cell battery.

(2)   By heat as in a thermocouple.

(3)   Mechanically, as in a generator.

The difference in electrical pressure which exists between any two points in the circuit is known as the potential difference (P.D.), as distinct from the total E.M.F. required to drive the current through the complete circuit.

(b) Current
The current in a circuit is the rate of flow of electricity. The practical unit of quantity of electricity is the Coulomb, which is approximately equal to 6.3×10^{18} electrons. Therefore the current in a circuit is the number of coulombs per second flowing past a definite point in that circuit.

(c) Resistance
The opposition to the flow of electrons in a conductor in an electrical circuit is known as resistance, and it is measured in ohms. Resistance depends on three factors:

(1)   The cross sectional area of the conductor.

(2)   The length of the conductor.

(3)   The material from which the conductor is manufactured.

Therefore, where it is required to keep the opposition to the flow of the electricity to a minimum, the conductor with the largest practical cross sectional area, the shortest length, and made from a low resistant material, such as copper, is used.

Conductors made of high resistance materials, such as eureka, which offer considerable resistance to the flow of electricity, are deliberately used as resistances where it is required to resist, or restrict, the flow of current.

It must be noted that the resistance of a conductor is only constant at constant temperature. The resistance of all pure metals increases with increased temperature, while that of carbon reduces. The fraction by which the resistance increases of a conductor for each degree centigrade rise of temperature above a definite temperature (usually 20°C) is called the temperature coefficient of resistance of the material.

2.4 Units of Measurement

(a) Standard Units

The value of the three conditions noted above is expressed by the following standard units:

(1) The Volt is the unit of difference of electrical pressure. A Potential Difference (P.D.) of one volt exists between two points in an electrical circuit, when one Joule of work is done in moving one Coulomb of electricity from one point to the other.

(2) The Ampere is the unit of rate of flow of electric current. A current of one ampere is the rate of flow of electricity of one coulomb per second past a definite point in the circuit.

(3) The Ohm is the unit of resistance. It is that resistance which permits a current of one ampere to flow when a P.D. of one volt is applied across it.

(4) Multiple and Submultiple Units. In addition to the standard units, it is convenient to have larger and smaller units of measurements. The relationship between such multiples and submultiples and the standard unit is indicated by the use of the following prefixes:

2.5 Ohms Law

In a D.C. (Direct Current) electrical circuit the ratio between the applied electrical pressure and the current flowing is constant at constant temperature. That is:

$\dfrac{E}{I}$ is a constant, and this constant is the resistance of the conductor.

This relationship between E.M.F. current and resistance is expressed by 'Ohms Law' which states that the current in a circuit is directly proportional to the pressure and inversely proportional to the pressure and inversely proportional to the resistance of the circuit. Thus, other factors remaining constant, if the pressure is doubled the current is doubled; if the resistance is doubled the current is halved. Ohms Law can be expressed as equation:

$$\text{Current in Amperes} = \frac{\text{E.M.F. in Volts}}{\text{Resistance in Ohms}}$$

In symbols $I = \dfrac{E}{R}$

If any two of these quantities are known therefore the third can be found by transposing the symbols, i.e.:

$R = \dfrac{E}{I}$ or $E = IR$ or $I \times R$.

2.6 Resistance in Simple Circuits.

(a) Series Connection

Conductors connected end to end so as to form a single circuit are said to be series. In a series circuit the value of the current is the same at all points and depends on the total resistance of the circuit and the applied E.M.F. The P.D. across each resistance is proportional to the value of that resistance.

Total resistance of several resistances in series is equal to the sum of the individual resistances, i.e.:

R_t $r_1 + r_2 + r_3 + \ldots$

(b) Parallel Connections

Conductors joined so that they provide alternative paths for the current are said to be in 'parallel'. In a parallel circuit the voltage is common to each path, and the current in each path is proportional to the resistance of that path. The total current equals the sum of the individual current. If several resistances are connected in parallel, the reciprocal of their total resistance $\dfrac{I}{R}$ is equal to the reciprocals of the individual resistances, i.e.:

$\dfrac{I}{R_t}$ $\dfrac{I}{r_1}\ \dfrac{I}{r_2}\ \dfrac{I}{r_3}\ \dfrac{I}{r_4}$

The total resistance which is calculated from the above expression, is always less than the lowest value of the individual resistances.

Note: Any one path is a shunt to the remainder.

See Figure 2-1 for examples.

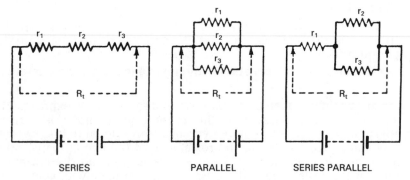

SERIES   PARALLEL   SERIES PARALLEL

Fig.2-1. Resistance arrangements.

(c) Series Parallel Combinations

To find the total resistance of a circuit containing both parallel and series connections, first find the equivalent value resistance of the parallel banks, as described previously in 2.6 (b), and then add this to the total value of other resistances connected in series.

2.7 Voltage Drop

When current flows, energy is absorbed in overcoming the resistance of the conductor and this energy is converted into heat. The loss of electrical energy results in a drop in electrical pressure along the conductor known as voltage drop. This difference in pressure between two points in a circuit is measured in volts. (E).

Voltage drop in a circuit is calculated by ohms law, i.e. E IR. It is important in circuits carrying heavy loads, that is, heavy currents, since a large current (I) causes a correspondingly large voltage drop.

Since voltage drop occurs in cables, the effective voltage at the terminals of equipment connected to the ends of those cables is less than the applied voltage at the supply ends is calculated as follows:

Effective voltage = Applied Voltage − Voltage Drop.

Therefore when wiring circuits the current carrying capacity of the cables must be sufficiently large in comparison with the current flowing to avoid excessive voltage drop and overheating of the cables.

2.8 Power and Energy

(a) Power
Power is the term used for the rate of doing work. The electrical unit of power is the Watt, and the power available from a source of supply is the product of E.M.F. in Volts and the current in Amperes, i.e., Watts = Volts × Amps or Power E × I watts.

Where the value of the voltage is not known, power can be calculated from the expression:

Power = I^2 R watts (since E = IR).

or if the current is not known,

Power = $\dfrac{E^2}{R}$ (since I $\dfrac{E}{R}$)

The equation Power = I^2R also represents the power lost in overcoming the resistance of the conductor and in producing heat.

The watt is too small for practical use where the power involved is large, and the unit adopted therefore is the kilowatt (1000 watts).

The mechanical unit of power, the Horse Power, is equivalent to 746 watts.

Therefore a kilowatt = $\dfrac{1000 \text{ watts}}{746}$ = 1.34 horse power.

(b) Energy
Energy is the capacity for doing work, It is therefore measured in the same units as are used for work, i.e. Joules, and is represented by the symbol W (Work).

The Joule is defined as the work done when a current of one ampere flows between any two points in one second due to a pressure of one volt. The power expended will thus be one watt, and hence 1 Joule = 1 watt-second and

W = I^2Rt joules (or watt seconds).

A more convenient unit than the watt-second is the Watt Hour which is defined as one watt supplied continuously for one hour.

For aircraft use the most common term used is the kilowatt hour, and is equivalent to 1000 watt-hours.

2.9 Magnetism

(a) Properties
If a steel bar is magnetised it acquires the following properties:

(1) The ends attract pieces of iron and steel. These ends where the force of attraction is greatest are known as the poles of the magnet.

(2) The bar if freely suspended from its centre, will always come to rest in the direction of the earth's magnetic field. The pole which seeks the north pole of the earth is known as the north pole, and the other the south pole.

(3) If a second magnet is brought near the suspended magnet the latter is either attracted or repelled according to the pole presented to it. Like poles repel and unlike poles attract each other.

(b) Magnetic Field
A field of magnetic influence exists in the space surrounding a magnet. As the distance from the magnet increases the strength of the magnetic field decreases. The magnetic field is represented in a diagram by lines of force, of flux, which are assumed to have the following properties:

(1) The tend to contract in length.

(2) They never cross.

(3) They are deflected by, and tend to pass through, magnetic materials placed in the magnetic field. In doing so they induce magnetic properties in that material.

(4) They form a complete magnetic circuit running from a north pole to a south pole outside the magnet and completing the loop from the south pole to the north pole through the magnet.

(c) Magnetic Materials
Soft iron and steel are the main magnetic materials used to construct magnets.

(1) Soft iron is easily magnetised, but loses the greater part of its magnetism when the magnetising force is removed. It is used in electro-magnets.

(2) Steel retains the greater part of its magnetism and is used for permanent magnets. Steel is usually alloyed with the practically non-magnetic materials tungsten, chromium and cobalt, which give it still better magnetic properties.

(d) Definitions
The following terms and symbols will be encountered in dealing with magnetic circuits and materials:

(1) Flux Density
The strength of the magnetic field, i.e. the number of lines of force per square centimetre.

(2) Permeability

The property of the magnetic material of increasing flux density; it may be compared with conductivity in the electric circuit. The permeability of air is unity, while that of soft iron and steel varies between 200 and 1000.

(3) Reluctance

This may be compared withe the resistance in an electric circuit. The reluctance of a magnetic circuit is greatly increased by the existence of air gaps, and in electric machines air gaps are normally kept as small as possible.

(4) Saturation

A magnetic material has reached its saturation when it is completely magnetised, i.e. when flux density cannot be further increased.

(5) Retentivity

The property possessed by a material of retaining magnetism after the magnetising force has been removed.

(6) Hysteresis

This is the lagging behind of magnetisation in a material as the magnetising force is removed, or reduced. The amount of magnetism retained by a material after the magnetising force has been removed is known as residual magnetism.

2.10   Effects of an Electric Current

The effects of the flow of electric current may be grouped under three headings:

(a) Magnetic Field

Current flowing through a conductor sets up a magnetic field. The direction of the current flow, and the direction of the lines of force around the conductor bear the same relationship to each other as do the thrust and the turn of a corkscrew.

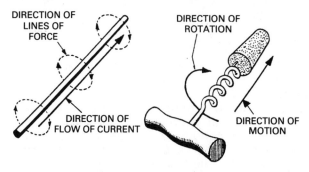

Fig.2-2. Corkscrew rule.

If a conductor carrying current, instead of being straight as above, is wound in the form of a coil or solenoid, a magnetic field is produced in and around the coil. The form of the field is similar to that of a bar magnet.

The polarity can be determined by imagining the solenoid to be grasped with the right hand, the fingers pointing in the direction of the current. The thumb then indicates the North pole. The polarity of the field reverses if the direction of current is reversed, and entirely disappears when the current is switched off.

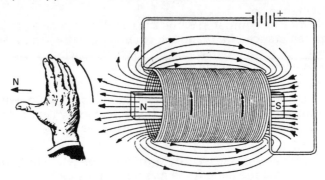

Fig.2-3. Polarity of a solenoid.

The strength of the magnetic field depends on the following factors:

(1) The current in amperes.

(2) The number of turns comprising the coil.

(3) The length of the coil.

(4) The permeability of the core.

Thus in an air-cored coil the flux density (B) is proportional to the magnetising force (H) expressed in ampere-turns per centimetre, i.e. product of the current in amperes and number of turns in each centimetre length of the coil. Most electro-magnets consists of a solenoid wound on a core of soft iron or similar magnetic material, which offers an easier path to the lines of force; the flux density due to the ampere-turns/centimetre is thus increased by an amount depending on the permeability of the core.

Electro-magnets are used in relay switches and motor and generator field systems, the chief advantages of this type of magnet being a stronger magnetic field, which can also be controlled by variation of the current.

(b) Heating Effect

    When current flows in a conductor the electrical power absorbed in overcoming resistance is converted into heat, causing a rise in temperature of the conductor. A steady temperature is reached when the heat lost per second by radiation, conduction and convection is equal to the heat gained per second from the current. The expression I^2RT joules (see paragraph 2.8, sub paragraph [a]) shows that the energy converted into heat is proportional to the product of the square of the current, the resistance in ohms, and the time in seconds (Joule's law). Since 1 joule = 0.24 calories of heat, therefore:

Heat developed = $I^2Rt \times 0.24$ calories.

The actual rise in temperature depends on the nature of the conductor, i.e. its dimensions and the material of which it is made. For example, the rise in temperature is greater:

(1) In a thin wire than in a thick wire carrying the same current.

(2) In an iron wire than in a copper wire of the same gauge and carrying the same current.

Hence in general wiring the current carrying capacity of a conductor must always be sufficiently large in relationship to the current flowing to prevent damage to the insulation of the conductor due to rise in temperature. Also electrical machines must be adequately ventilated or otherwise cooled to prevent overheating.

This heating effect is deliberately used in lamp filaments, heater elements and hot-wire ammeters.

(c) Chemical Effect

Certain substances, such as salts and acids, when dissolved in water conduct electricity and are known as electrolytes; dilute sulphuric acid is a typical electrolyte. The conductors by which the current enters and leaves the solution are known as electrodes and are termed the anode and cathode respectively. The passage of the current decomposes the solution into its constituent ions, the process being known as electrolysis. These ions are of two kinds, some being negatively charged and the others positively charged. The former are attracted towards the positive anode, whilst the latter travel with the current towards the cathode. Gases are also evolved at the electrodes.

This principle is applied in electro-plating, the essentials being an anode of the plating metal and an electrolyte suitable for the type of plating; the article to be plated forms the cathode. The passage of current takes metal out of the electrolyte and deposits it on the cathode; at the same time an equal amount of metal is dissolved from the anode into the electrolyte. The amount of metal deposited is proportional to the current and the time for which it flows. The amount of any particular metal deposited by one coulomb of electricity is known as the electro-chemical equivalent of the ion of that metal.

Other practical applications of the chemical effect of electric current are secondary cells and electrolytic meters. In the latter case the current flow is calculated by the amount of metal deposited, i.e.:

$$I = \frac{\text{Weight of metal deposited}}{\text{Electro-chemical equivalent} \times \text{time in seconds}}$$

Hence the definition of the ampere as that current, which will deposit 0.001118 gramme of silver per second from a solution of silver nitrate.

2.11 Electro-magnetic Induction

The principle of electro-magnetic induction is that used in electrical machines whenever an electric current is produced by means of a magnetic field. When a permanent magnet is lowered into a coil (see diagram), lines of force cut the turns of wire. If the two ends of the coil are connected to a galvanometer the instrument pointer is deflected, indicating that an E.M.F. is being induced in the coil and that current is flowing. The pointer returns to the central position as soon as the relative motion between the magnet and coil ceases. This relative motion must always be such that the lines of force move across the conductors at an angle; if they move parallel to the conductors no E.M.F. is induced.

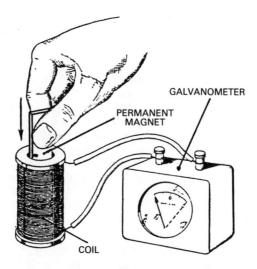

Fig.2-4. Electro-magnetic induction.

When the magnet is withdrawn the pointer is again deflected, but in the opposite direction. In both cases the direction of the induced current is such that the electro magnetic field opposes the movement of the magnet.

The principles of electro-magnetic induction are summarised by two laws:

(a) Faraday's Law
Which states that the value of the induced E.M.F. is proportional to the rate of change of flux linkage, e.g. an E.M.F. of 1 volt is induced when the rate of change is

100,000,000 (i.e. 10^8) lines of force per second.

(b) Lenz's Law
Which states that in electro-magnetic induction the induced currents have such a direction that their reaction tends to stop the motion which produces them.

2.12 Inductance

Inductance (symbol L) is the property possessed by any circuit such as a

16

coil, where a change of current is accompanied by a change in the strength of a magnetic field.

(a) Self-Inductance

When the current through a coil varies, the resultant movement of the surrounding lines of magnetic force induces an E.M.F. in the turns of the coil. This induced E.M.F. is in such a direction that it opposes the changing condition in the circuit (Lenz's law). Thus on closing the switch in an inductive D.C. circuit the self-induced (or back-) E.M.F. opposes the applied E.M.F. and causes a gradual rise in current to its maximum steady value, while the magnetic field surrounding the coil is being established. On opening the switch the collapse of the magnetic field tends to maintain the flow of current, and if a resistance is connected in parallel with the inductance a decaying current flows through it while the energy stored in the magnetic field is being returned to the circuit (see diagram). If there is no resistance in parallel the tendency to maintain the flow of current creates an arc at the switch contacts at the instant of opening.

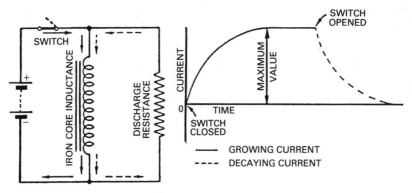

Fig.2-5. Current in inductive circuit (Growth and Decay)

The unit of inductance is the Henry (H) and a circuit has an inductance of 1 Henry if an E.M.F. of 1 volt is induced in the circuit when the current changes at the rate of 1 ampere per second.

Iron-cored inductances or chokes are generally used in rectifier circuits for smoothing out variations in direct current obtained from an A.C. supply.

(b) Mutual Inductance

If two coils are placed so that when current is passed through one of them the resultant magnetic flux links with the other coil, any variation of the current in the first coil causes an E.M.F. to be induced in the second coil. The coils are known as the primary and secondary coils respectively, and are said to have mutual inductance. The unit of measurement is the Henry, and the mutual inductance of two coils is 1 Henry when an E.M.F. of 1 volt is induced in the secondary due to the primary current changing at the rate of 1 ampere per second.

The principle is used in transformers (see Section 2 Chapter 2), ignition coils, magnetos and similar apparatus.

2.13 The Condenser

Any two conductors separated by an insulator form a condenser (or capacitator) and, when a P.D. is applied across them, have the property of storing an electric charge; this property is known as capacitance.

The simple condenser consists of two sheets of metal foil separated by a thin strip of waxed paper or mica, termed the plates and the dielectric respectively. When a momentary current flows into the condenser a P.D. is established across its plates. Since the dielectric contains no free electrons this current cannot flow through it, but the P.D. sets up a state of stress in the atoms comprising it. For example, in the circuit shown below, on placing the switch in position 1 a rush of electrons — known as the charging current — occurs from plate A through the accumulator to plate B, and ceases when the P.D. between the plates is equal to the P.D. of the accumulator. When the switch is opened the plates remain positively and negatively charged respectively, since the atoms of plate A have lost electrons while those at B have a surplus; thus electrical energy is stored in the condenser in the form of an electric field existing between the plates due to the force of attraction between the opposite charges on them. When the switch is moved to position 2 the plates are short-circuited and the surplus electrons at the negatively charged plate rush back to the positively charged plate until the atoms of both plates are electrically neutral and no P.D. exists between them. This discharging current is in the reverse direction to the charging current as indicated by the centre-zero ammeter.

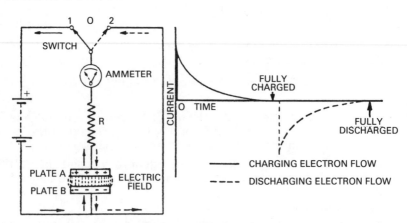

Fig.2-6. Condenser principle.

Both the charging and discharging currents are maximum at the commencement of charge and discharge respectively, and gradually fall to zero. Increase in the value of the resistance (R) decreases the initial maximum value of the current, but increases the duration of the charge and discharge; this principle is used in time bases. Note that the current only flows when applied P.D. is changing.

Excessive P.D. across the plates causes a spark to occur between them and punctures the insulation, i.e. the condenser 'breaks down'. The maximum permissible working voltage (D.C.) is therefore marked on condensers, and depends on the thickness and dielectric strength of the insulating material used.

2.14 Capacitance

The capacitance (C) of a condenser is the ratio between the charge in coulombs (Q) retained by the condenser and the P.D. in volts between the plates, i.e.:

$$\text{Capacitance in Farads} = \frac{\text{Charge in coulombs}}{\text{P.D. in volts}} \text{ or } C = \frac{Q}{V}$$

The Farad (F) is the unit of capacitance and is the capacitance of a condenser in which a charge of 1 coulomb raises the P.D. between the plates by one volt. The Farad is too large for practical values and the microfarad (mid. or μF = 10^{-6}F.) is generally used.

(a) Capacitance of Condenser

The capacitance of a condenser is directly proportional to:

(1) The area of the plates: e.g. the greater the number of plates connected in parallel the larger the capacitance.

(2) The dielectric constant of the insulator between the plates: e.g. that of air is unity, and that of mica 5 (approximately).

and is inversely proportional to:

(3) The thickness of the dielectric: the thinner the dielectric the greater the capacitance for the same area of plate.

(b) Condensers in Parallel

Since the effective area of the plates is increased, the total capacity is increased, and is the sum of the individual capacities, i.e.:

$$C_t = C_1 + C_2 + C_3 + \text{etc.}$$

(c) Condensers in Series

Since the thickness of the dielectric is increased the total capacity is decreased, being less than the capacity of any one of the individual condensers. It is calculated by the expression:

$$\frac{1}{C_t} = \frac{1}{C_1} + \frac{1}{C_2} + \frac{1}{C_3} + \text{etc.}$$

CHAPTER 2
TEST YOURSELF QUESTIONS

1. Resistance in a conductor:
   (a) increases with increase of temperature.
   (b) reduces with increase of temperature.
   (c) remains constant at all temperatures.
   (d) varies in an irregular manner with temperature change.

   Ref. Ch.2. Para.2.3.

2. Electrical pressure:
   (a) is measured in amps.
   (b) is the E.M.F.
   (c) is the rate of current flow.
   (d) is measured in ohms.

   Ref. Ch.2. Para.2.3.

3. The rate of doing work of an electrical component is measured in:
   (a) volts.
   (b) ohms.
   (c) amps.
   (d) watts.

   Ref. Ch.2. Para.2.8.

4. Energy:
   (a) is the voltage available.
   (b) is the current rate.
   (c) is the capacity for doing work.
   (d) is the capacity to store power.

   Ref. Ch.2. Para.2.8.

5. Resistance is:
   (a) $E \times I$.
   (b) $R - I$.
   (c) $E - I$.
   (d) $\dfrac{E}{I}$

   Ref. Ch.2. Para.2.5.

3

ELEMENTARY PRINCIPLES OF D.C. GENERATORS AND MOTORS

3.1 Electro-magnetic Induction

A generator is a machine which converts mechanical power into electric power. It consists of a magnetic field in which conductors are rotated in such a manner that they cut the magnetic lines of force.

If a conductor is moved in a magnetic field, in such a manner that it cuts lines of force, an E.M.F. is induced in that conductor. In a similar manner if the conductor is held stationary and the magnetic field is moved or varied in intensity, an E.M.F. is induced in the conductor. A voltmeter connected across the two ends of the conductor will read the value of the E.M.F. induced, and if a closed circuit is connected across the two ends of the conductor a current will flow.

Fleming's Right-Hand Rule is a simple means of determining the direction of an induced E.M.F. If the first finger of the right hand is pointed in the direction of the magnetic field, and the thumb in the direction of motion of the conductor relative to the magnetic field, then the middle finger, held at right angles to both the thumb and first finger, indicates the direction of the E.M.F. and current.

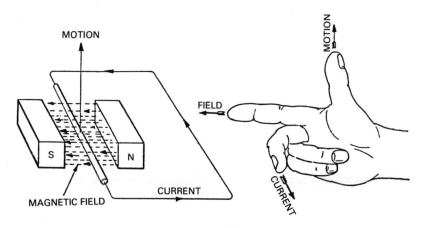

Fig.3-1. Fleming's Right-Hand Rule.

3.2 E.M.F. Induced in a Rotating Loop

The simplest form of generator consists of a loop of wire, known as an armature, rotating in a permanent magnetic field. Connection to the external circuit is made by brushes pressing on two slip rings connected to the ends of the coil (see Fig.3-2).

During rotation the two sides of the loop cut the magnetic field in opposite directions. The E.M.Fs. induced are therefore in opposite directions, but, since the conductor forms a complete loop, they assist each other, so that the total E.M.F. — across the slip rings — is the sum of the two. The value of the E.M.F. varies during rotation, according to the number of lines of force cut by the conductors during a given time; this depends on the angle at which the conductors are moving across the magnetic field, and on the speed of rotation.

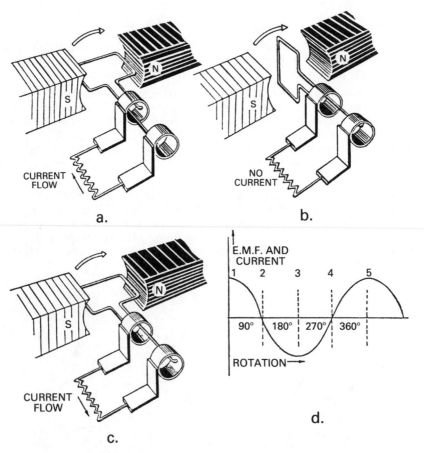

Fig.3-2. Production of alternating current.

In Fig.3-2a the sides of the loop are moving at right angles to the field, cutting the maximum number of lines of force, and the induced E.M.F. is at a maximum in one direction: This corresponds to position 1 in

Fig.3-2d which shows the rise and fall of the induced E.M.F. As the loop rotates the induced E.M.F. falls, until the sides of the loop are moving parallel to the field as at Fig.3-2b when for an instant no lines of force are cut and the E.M.F. is zero; this corresponds to position 2 in Fig.3-2d. Continued rotation causes the sides of the loop to move into the field and the E.M.F. rises until it again reaches a maximum, in the position shown in Fig.3-2.c. Since the relative motion between each side of the loop and the magnetic field was reversed at the position shown in Fig.3-2d, this second maximum E.M.F. is in the opposite direction to the first maximum and is shown at position 3 in Fig.3-2d. With continued rotation the sides of the loop once again move parallel to the magnetic field, and as no lines of force are being cut, the induced E.M.F. again falls to zero as at postion 4. After one complete revolution the loop reaches its original position in the field and the E.M.F. is once again maximum as at position 5.

The direction of the E.M.F. and polarity of the slip rings therefore reverse as the sides of the loop move alternately under the influence of a north and south pole. The direction of the current flow in the external circuit therefore also changes direction and is known as an alternating current.

3.3   Production of Direct Current

To change the alternating current in the rotating loop into a uni-directional or direct current in the external circuit, the ends of the loop are connected to the two halves of a split ring. This forms a simple commutator, the two halves being insulated from each other and known as segments. The loop is connected to the external circuit by two brushes placed on opposite sides of the commutator.

In Fig.3-3a no E.M.F. is induced in the loop and no current flows in the external circuit. In Fig.3-3b maximum E.M.F. is induced in the loop and current flows in the external circuit in the direction indicated. In Fig.3-3c the E.M.F. has fallen to zero and the segments are moving on to the opposite brushes. In Fig.3-3d the E.M.F. in the loop has risen to a maximum in the opposite direction, but since the commutator segments are under opposite brushes the current flows in the same direction in the external circuit. Fig 3-3e completes one revolution and the E.M.F. is again zero.

The current always flows in the same direction in the external circuit, one brush always being positive and the other always negative.

The E.M.F. and current produced by a single loop falls to zero twice per revolution. A smoother flow of current can be obtained by increasing the number of loops and commutator segments. The loops are placed symmetrically around the axis of rotation. The E.M.F. induced in each loop therefore reaches its maximum value slightly later than the preceding loop. The resultant E.M.F. at the brushes is fairly steady, and at no time falls to zero. The fluctuation in voltage becomes a ripple as indicated by the heavy line in the illustration (Fig.3-4).

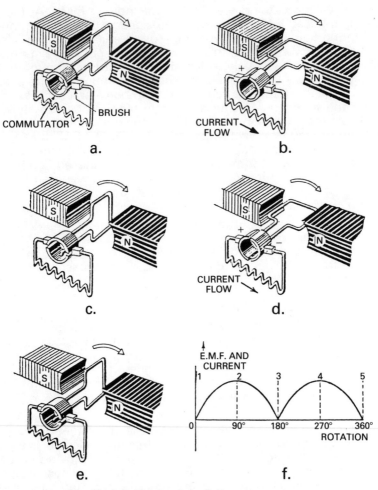

Fig.3-3. Production of direct current.

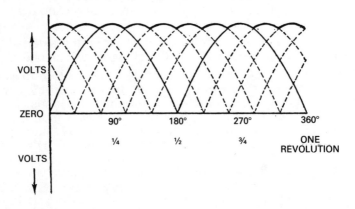

Fig.3-4. Voltage produced by several armature coils.

3.4 Magnitude of the E.M.F.

The E.M.F. induced in a single loop of wire moving in a permanent magnetic field is too small to be of practical use. A higher E.M.F. can be obtained by using a coil of wire, consisting of several turns, each end being connected to a separate commutator's segment; this is known as an armature coil. The E.M.F.s induced in the separate turns are all in the same direction, and combine to form a total E.M.F. at the brushes, equal to the sum of the E.M.F.s induced in each turn of the coil.

If an electro-magnet is used in place of the permanent magnet, variation of the current flowing through the magnet coils changes the strength of the magnetic field. For any given speed of rotation of the armature, the induced E.M.F. increases or decreases as the field strength is increased or decreased. If the speed of rotation is increased or decreased so a greater or smaller number of lines of force are cut in a given time and the induced E.M.F. increases or decreases.

Therefore the magnitude of an induced E.M.F. depends on three factors:

(a) Number of conductors.

(b) Speed of rotation.

(c) Strength of the magnetic field.

In practice the number of conductors is fixed by the designer, and machines are usually driven at a constant speed by a governor controlled prime-mover. The voltage is therefore usually controlled by varying the field strength by means of a variable resistance in the field circuit.

CONSTRUCTION OF D.C. MACHINES

3.5 The Magnetic Field System

To obtain an intense magnetic field D.C. machines are constructed of magnetic materials. With the exception of a small air gap, separating the rotating armature from the stationary field system, a complete magnetic circuit is formed. The component parts of the magnetic field are as follows:

(a) The Yoke is the circular frame of the machine and is made of cast iron, cast steel or rolled steel.

(b) The Pole Pieces are built up of steel laminations, and bolted on the inside of the yoke. Solid mild steel pole pieces with laminated pole shoes are sometimes used.

(c) The Field Windings are wound round the pole pieces, in such a manner that the polarity of adjacent poles is alternatively North and South.

(d) The Armature Core is made up of thin iron laminations, mounted on a cast iron spider keyed to the shaft. It is slotted to take the armature windings and rotates inside the pole shoes, being separated from them by a small air gap.

3.6 The Armature

The armature is the practical application of the rotating loop of wire. It consists of a number of coils wound on the armature core; these are rotated in the magnetic field by a prime mover such as a petrol engine or electric motor; it includes the following parts:

(a) Armature Windings

In small machines each armature coil consists of several turns of d.c.c. wire, which are wound on a former to the correct shape. The coil is then insulated with varnished cambric and is fitted in the armature slots, which are lined with thin fibre. In larger machines copper strip conductors are used. Each end of each armature coil is connected to a separate segment of the commutator.

As the armature rotates centrifugal force tends to throw the armature coils outwards. This is prevented by wire lapping, which holds the conductors in position in the armature slots.

(b) The Commutator

This is mounted at one end of the armature shaft and is built up of copper segments, insulated from each other by thin mica sheets. The whole assembly is insulated from but rotates with the armature shaft. The number of segments is equal to the number of armature coils. The armature coils are connected to the commutator by thin strips of copper known as 'risers' and soldered into slots in the segments.

(c) Exhaust Fan

For cooling purposes a fan is mounted on the opposite end of the armature shaft to the commutator.

(d) The Bearings

In large machines the armature shaft rotates in plain journal bearings in the end plates. Small machines are usually fitted with ball or roller-bearings at each end.

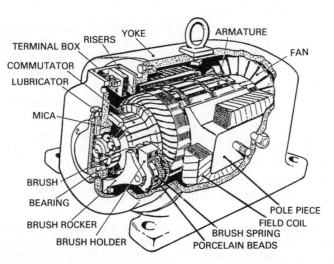

Fig.3-5. Construction of a D.C. machine.

3.7 Brushgear

Since the armature is rotating a rubbing contact is necessary to carry current away from the moving commutator and conductors, to the stationary external circuit. This is provided by the brushgear, which consists of the following parts:

(a) Brushes

These are usually made of carbon or graphite, and sometimes a mixture of copper and carbon to increase conductivity. When they are set radially to the commutator, the armature can be rotated in either direction. When the brushes are set at an angle to the commutator, the armature must be rotated in one direction only. The brushes are connected to the terminals by flexible copper leads, sometimes insulated with porcelain beads.

(b) Brush Holders

These are small brackets or boxes in which the brushes are mounted. A spring is fitted, which presses the brush on to the surface of the commutator, ensuring good electrical contact.

(c) Brush Rocker

The brush holders are sometimes mounted on an adjustable ring or rocker. The whole assembly may be turned relative to the commutator, until the brushes are in the best position for good commutation, with the minimum of sparking. This is known as rocking the brushes. The normal position is usually indicated by marks on the brush rocker and end frame.

Note:

Where four brushes are fitted, they are alternately positive and negative, those of the same polarity being connected to each other.

TYPES OF D.C. GENERATOR

3.8 Method of Field Excitation

Some small generators such as magnetos use a permanent magnetic field, but most generators have an electro-magnetic field. The following diagram shows a four-pole machine. The four brushes are resting on the commutator. The two positive brushes are connected together and to the positive terminal A. The negative brushes are also connected together and to the negative terminal AA (or A_1).

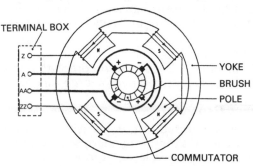

Fig.3-6. Armature and field connections.

The four field coils are usually connected in series and referred to as the field circuit, the ends being connected to the terminals Z and ZZ (or Z_1). The coils are so wound and connected that the poles are alternately North and South.

There are several methods of supplying the field current, and the characteristic of the generator largely depends on the method of field excitation. The characteristic of a generator is the relationship between the voltage at the generator terminals and the load current. In general the voltage of a generator tends to fall as the load current increases. Generators are named according to the manner in which the field and armature windings are connected; the various types are described in the following paragraphs.

3.9 Separately Excited Generator

The field winding is connected to an external source of supply such as a small D.C. generator known as the exciter. The field current remains constant irrespective of the load connected to the generator. When a load is switched on current flows through the armature, therefore the terminal voltage falls slightly as the load is increased due to voltage drop in the armature windings.

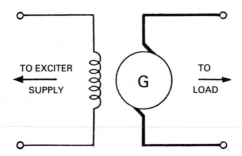

Fig.3-7. Separately excited generator.

(a) Voltage Regulation

The current flowing through the field circuit, and therefore the strength of the magnetic field, can be controlled by varying the voltage of the exciter. If the armature speed is kept constant, increase in the field current causes an increase in the generated E.M.F.; decreased field current causes a decrease in the generated E.M.F.

(b) Use

This type of machine is used where complete control of the field current and voltage is required over a large range.

3.10 Shunt-Wound Generator

The field winding is connected in parallel with the armature and with the external load circuit. It is therefore energised by part of the armature current, The field coils contain a large number of turns of wire and are of relatively high resistance, thus taking a small current.

When the armature is rotated the conductors cut the weak magnetic field due to the residual magnetism in the poles. A small E.M.F. is generated and, since the field is connected across the armature, a current flows through the field coils, thus increasing the magnetic flux. This causes a further rise in E.M.F. and a further rise in field current and so on. Therefore the field is fully excited, when no external load is connected, and the terminal voltage is at a maximum. A shunt generator must be allowed to 'build up' before connecting the load.

Variation of the load on a shunt generator causes a small variation in the terminal voltage; as the load increases the voltage falls. If a constant load is applied the terminal voltage takes up a steady value. If the generator is overloaded the voltage falls considerably.

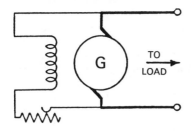

Fig.3-8. Shunt-wound generator.

(a) Voltage Regulation
This is obtained by inserting a variable resistance known as a field regulating resistance (Voltage Regulator) in series with the field winding as shown in the diagram. Variation of the resistance increases or decreases the field current, causing a corresponding variation of the magnetic field and therefore of the generated E.M.F.

(b) Use
Shunt generators are used to supply loads such as accumulator charging. They are used as engine driven generators on aircraft.

3.11 Series-Wound Generator

The field winding is connected in series with the armature and load, therefore the current flowing in the series field is the load current. To reduce voltage drop in the field, the resistance of the winding is low and the number of turns small. Since the field is in series with the armature no current flows through it until an external circuit is connected. On open circuit the small E.M.F. generated is due to residual magnetism in the field system.

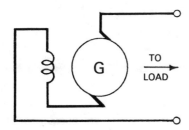

Fig.3-9. Series-wound generator.

As the load is increased more current flows through the field coils and increases the strength of the magnetic field. Therefore in a series machine the terminal voltage increases almost proportionately with increase in load current until the maximum output is reached.

The generator is unsuitable for normal use and has no service application. In mains supply systems it is sometimes necessary to compensate for resistance drop in long cables, and a series generator can be connected in series with the main circuit to step-up the voltage; these generators are known as boosters.

3.12   Compound-Wound Generator

In this type of generator a combination of shunt and series field excitation is used. The machine has a shunt winding connected in parallel with the armature, with a low resistance series winding — connected in series with the load — producing the same polarity and wound on the same pole pieces. As the load is increased the current in the series winding increases, resulting in an increased field strength, which compensates for the fall in voltage, which occurs in a plain shunt generator (see paragraph 10). If the series winding is so designed that the terminal voltage is maintained almost constant, the machine is said to be 'level-compounded'. If the number of turns is greater the voltage rises as the load is increased and the machine is said to be 'over-compounded'.

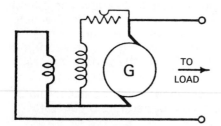

Fig.3-10. Compound-wound generator.

(a) Voltage Regulation

A rheostat is connected in series with the shunt field circuit. It is used for small voltage adjustments by increasing or decreasing the field current. Its range is usually smaller than in a shunt machine, as the main voltage regulation is automatically carried out by the series field winding.

(b) Use

This is the most common form of industrial generator and is used for fluctuating loads such as lighting and traction. A level-compounded generator is used wherever a constant terminal voltage is required with varying loads. When power is transmitted over long distances, an over-compound generator is used to compensate for voltage drop in the cables, and to maintain a constant voltage at the end of the feeders.

3.13   Rating

The rating of a generator is the output in watts or kilowatts that a machine will supply; this is limited by the rise in temperature, which occurs in the machine due to electrical losses. The rating is calculated by the maker and is given, either directly in watts or indirectly in amps and volts (watts = amps × volts), on the rating plate attached to the machine; it gives all or part of the following information:

(a) Number of the generator and its type of winding.

(b) Voltage and type of supply (D.C. or A.C.).

(c) Pressure between terminals in volts.

(d) Current in amperes.

(e) Speed in revolutions per minute.

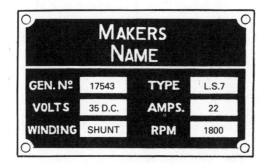

Fig.3-11. Rating plate.

The rating plate shows that the machine is a direct current, shunt-wound generator, with a normal working voltage of 35 volts and a maximum load of 22 amps, when it is driven at a speed of 1,800 r.p.m. Its rating is 35 volts × 22 amps = 770 watts.

3.14 Parallel Operation of Shunt Generators

In multi-engined aircraft shunt generators are sometimes connected in parallel so that the load is shared equally between them. The principle is illustrated in the diagram Fig.3-12, the generators are connected to common positive and negative mains through double pole switches. The terminal voltage of each generator is controlled by a Voltage Regulator. An ammeter and voltmeter are connected in each generator circuit.

One generator is run up to speed — the required voltage being obtained by adjusting the field regulating resistance — and is connected to the load by closing the double-pole switch. To bring the second generator into operation it must first be run up to speed, and its voltage adjusted to the same value as the first generator before closing its double-pole switch.

Adjust the field regulating resistance until the load is equally shared between the generators as indicated on the ammeters. If the voltage of one generator falls, the other generator drives current through it in a reverse direction, causing it to act as a motor. The whole load is thus thrown on to the first generator, which may consequently be overloaded.

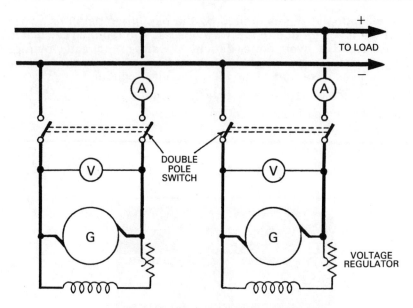

Fig.3-12. Shunt generators in parallel.

On disconnecting one generator, adjust the field regulating resistance until the ammeter reads zero before opening the double pole switch.

ELEMENTARY MOTOR PRINCIPLES

3.15 Action of a Motor

The electric motor is a machine for converting electrical energy into mechanical energy, its function being the reverse of a generator. There is no difference in construction between a D.C. generator and a D.C. motor and if an external supply is connected to the terminals of a D.C. machine current flows through the armature and field windings and the armature revolves.

The diagram shows one conductor, on the armature of a D.C. machine, under a North pole. Current is flowing in the conductor in the direction 'into the paper'. A magnetic field is set up round the conductor in a

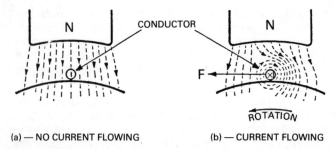

(a) — NO CURRENT FLOWING   (b) — CURRENT FLOWING

Fig.3-13. Motor principle.

clockwise direction (Corkscrew rule). It is seen that on the left of the conductor this field and the main magnetic field oppose one another; on the right-hand side they assist one another. The result is that lines of force of the main magnetic field Fig.3-13a become distorted Fig.3-13b. Bearing in mind the elastic properties of magnetic lines of force, and regarding them as stretched elastic threads, a mechanical force is exerted on the conductor in the direction F, and the armature rotates in an anti-clockwise direction.

Paragraph 3.1 of this section illustrates Fleming's Right-Hand Rule for a generator; in the same manner Fleming's Left-Hand Rule applies to a motor: the left hand first finger points in the direction of the magnetic field; the middle finger points in the direction of current flow in the conductor, the thumb shows the direction in which the conductor moves.

The action of the commutator reverses the direction of the flow of current in each armature conductor as it passes under the influence of the next pole, which is of opposite polarity. Thus the mechanical force on each conductor is always in the same direction and the armature continues to rotate so long as the supply is connected.

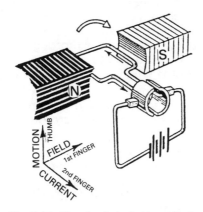

Fig.3-14. Fleming's Left-Hand Rule.

3.16   Back E.M.F.

The resistance of the armature windings of most motors is very low, usually being less than 1 ohm. If this was the only opposition offered to the current, in say a 220 volt supply, the current would be extremely high. This, however, is not the case. Immediately the armature of a motor starts rotating, the armature conductors cut the main magnetic field and an E.M.F. is induced in them as in a generator. This E.M.F. always opposes the E.M.F. applied to the terminals of the motor and is thus known as the 'Back E.M.F.' The current which actually flows through the armature therefore depends on the effective E.M.F., which is the difference between the applied E.M.F. and the back E.M.F.

3.17   Speed of a D.C. Motor

The speed and current consumption of a motor automatically adjust themselves to the mechanical load. When the load is increased the speed falls causing the back E.M.F. to fall also. The effective E.M.F. is therefore increased and a greater current is taken from the supply. This variation of speed with load is known as the 'speed characteristic' of the motor, and as in a generator this characteristic depends on the method by which the field is excited and motors are named accordingly.

The speed of a motor can be controlled over a wide range by variation of the current flowing through the field coils; this is done by connecting a variable resistance in the field circuit. In any D.C. motor, weakening of the field results in an increase in armature speed, whilst strengthening the field decreases the r.p.m.

TYPES OF D.C. MOTOR

3.18 Shunt Wound Motor

The field winding is connected in parallel with the armature. The field is therefore directly across the supply and it is of a fairly high resistance. If the supply voltage is maintained constant the field strength remains constant. The armature is also connected across the supply and since it is of low resistance, a shunt motor must not be started by connecting it directly to the mains as a heavy current will flow through the armature windings. To limit the starting current a resistance is connected in series with the armature until the speed of the motor generates sufficient back E.M.F. to limit the working current to a safe value. The driving power (torque) of a shunt motor is small on starting and on low speeds.

The speed of a shunt motor is controlled by a variable resistance connected in series with the shunt field windings. If the resistance in the circuit is increased the speed is increased and vice versa (see paragraph 3.19).

When a load is applied the reduction in speed from 'no load' to 'full load' is very small, and the shunt motor can be considered a constant speed machine. This type of motor is generally used where the load does not vary greatly and where an approximate constant speed is required, e.g. workshop lathes.

3.19 Series-Wound Motor

In this type of motor the armature and field windings are in series with each other so that — unlike the shunt motor — the armature and field currents are the same. The combined resistance of the armature and field is very small and a large current flows on starting. This can be controlled by a resistance — in series with the circuit — which is gradually cut out as the speed rises. For some purposes, e.g. engine starting, no starting resistance is used and the circuit is designed to carry heavy currents.

The speed of a series motor varies considerably with the mechanical load applied, running slowly on heavy loads and fast on light loads. It is important that a series motor be permanently connected to the load, as, if the load is removed, the motor races at dangerously high speeds.

Since this type of motor has a high starting torque it is used for engine starting, cranes and traction work.

3.20   Compound-Wound Motor

The motor has two field windings, one shunt connected and the other connected in series with the armature, both being wound on the same pole pieces. In the more common type of compound motor the series field is wound so that it produces the same polarity as the shunt field and as the load increases so the influence of the series field increases. A compound motor has a speed/load characteristic between that of a shunt and series motor depending on the relative strengths of the two windings.

If the influence of the series field is small the motor has a shunt characteristic at first, but as the load is increased the speed falls more rapidly than that of a shunt motor. If the series field is predominant the motor has a high starting torque — that is a series characteristic — but the small shunt winding limits the no load speed to a safe value.

The speed of a compound motor is controlled by connecting a variable resistance in series with the shunt field; as the resistance in circuit is increased the speed increases.

Compound motors are used to drive cranes and machinery, where the load fluctuates.

OPERATION OF D.C. SHUNT MOTORS

3.21   Motor Starter

To limit the current, when starting a D.C. machine, a variable resistance is placed in series with the armature. On starting the maximum resistance is in the circuit, and as the armature gathers speed the resistance is gradually decreased until it is finally cut out altogether.

Starter resistances used are usually of the faceplate type, with the components mounted on an insulated panel. The resistance is tapped at several points, which are connected to contact studs on the faceplate; a moving arm makes contact with these studs. The moving arm is normally held in the off position by a spring and is held in the full-on position by an electro-magnet known as the no-volt coil. An overload release consisting of an electro-magnetic or thermal switch is incorporated and releases the handle — which flies back to the off position — if an excessive current flows. Connections to the starter are made by three terminals marked Z (field), L (line) and A (armature).

3.22   Shunt Motor Installation

A D.C. shunt motor circuit consists of a main switch and fuses, starter, and in some cases a reversing switch. Before the supply is connected the motor, starter, and switch casings must be connected to a good earth. One line from the supply is connected through the main switch to the terminal L on the starter; the other line is connected to the terminals AA and ZZ on the motor. The A terminal on the starter is connected to the other side of the motor armature at A terminal, and the Z terminal is connected to the corresponding Z terminal (shunt field) on the motor.

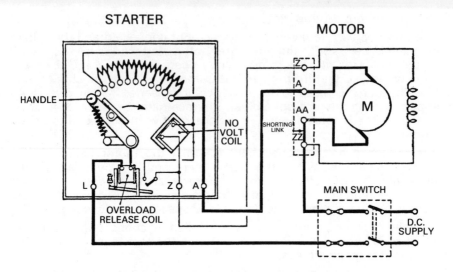

Fig.3-15. D.C. Shunt motor and starter.

3.23 Starting

Before starting, the speed regulator — if fitted — must be set in the position of minimum resistance. To start the motor close the main switch, and move the starter handle slowly from the OFF to the ON position, by which time the motor should be running at full speed.

3.24 The Basic D.C. Circuit

The following is a brief explanation of the principles and operation of a basic D.C. system. This should be read in conjunction with a study of Fig.3-16.

This system uses a shunt wound D.C. generator.

(a) Generator
   In order voltage can be induced into the armature loop, two basic functions are required:

   (1) The armature loop or conductor must be in motion, i.e. rotated.

   (2) A magnetic field must exist between the magnetic poles.

   The armature is rotated by the engine, normally via a drive shaft or a drive belt similar to a car generator drive system, causing the armature loop to cut the lines or magnetic force, or flux, between the magnetic poles.

   On engine starting the initial excitation, that is, the initial magnetic field, is provided by residual magnetism retained by permanent magnets within the core of the magnetic poles.

   Normal or operational excitation is provided by electro-magnetic coils or windings wound onto the magnetic poles and are known as the field windings.

   Current will not flow in the field windings, in the example shown, until the generator produces current flow, hence the need for initial excitation.

The generator produces Alternating Current which through the method of collection of the current through a Comultator, becomes D.C. More recent types of D.C. system may use a Rectifier to perform this function.

The flow of current from the generator, the generator output, will in the main be determined by the demands of the various circuits. The various circuits, or services, referred to service loads are connected to the bus-bar, the distribution point. The generator supplies its current to the bus-bar.

The output of the generator is indicated on an Ammeter, this measures the current flow in Amperes (Amps). The majority of the output flows to the bus-bar, some however flows to the field windings via the Voltage Regulator to create the required magnetic field.

Note:
The ammeter used to indicate generator output is normally termed the Load Ammeter or Generator Load Ammeter.

(b) The Voltage Regulator
The stronger the field current, that is current flowing to the field windings, the greater the output of the generator. The flow of current to the field windings is controlled by the voltage regulator which is a form of variable resistor.

The Voltage Regulator is designed to operate at a set value giving the generator a constant voltage or pressure output. Normally for each 12 volts required in the system the generator will produce 14 volts; i.e. for a 24 volt system the generator will produce 28 volts, etc. The additional output is required to make up for losses in the system and to provide enough additional voltage to recharge the battery in flight.

If the generator voltage is insufficient, it is said to be undervolting, if it is producing too greater output, it is said to be overvolting.

In operation therefore, if the generator is overvolting the magnetic field between the poles is too strong, the voltage regulator will then sense this from the generator output, increase its resistance, reduce the field current to the magnetic poles, and therefore reduce the output of the generator.

(c) Cut Out
Before the engine is started, electrical supply will be provided by the battery. This is achieved by switching on the Master Switch, and or, the Battery Master Switch. This action connects the battery to the bus-bar. As current will flow through the lines of least resistance, there is a danger the battery will discharge through the generator, possibly damaging its windings, rather than supply the bus-bar. To prevent the battery discharging to the generator, the Cut Out or Battery Cut Out is fitted.

As shown in simple form, the cut out has a switch which will remain open until the generator produces, usually ½ volt more than battery

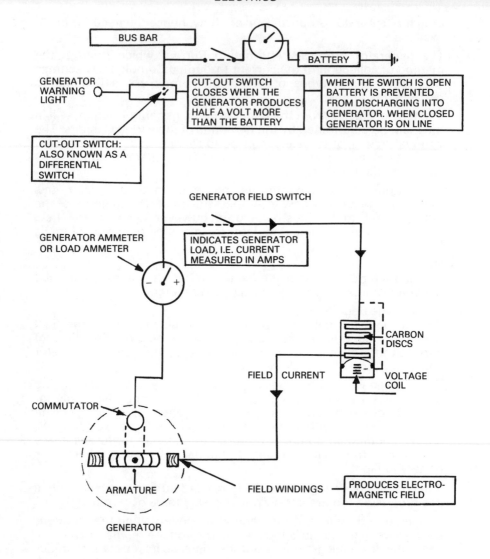

Fig.3-16. Basic D.C. supply switch.

output, and then the switch will close connecting the generator to the bus-bar. The generator can now be said to be 'on line', that is, when it is connected to the bus-bar.

(d) Generator Warning Light

The generator warning light is usually a red warning light displayed in the cockpit. It indicates when the generator fails or is not 'on line', that is, it is not connected to the bus-bar. It operates in conjunction with the cut out and unless the cut out switch is closed the warning light will illuminate.

(e) Battery Ammeter
The Battery Ammeter indicates the rate of charge or discharge of the battery.

(f) Batteries
With the exception of light aircraft, there is normally more than one battery fitted and they are virtually always fitted in parallel to provide a greater ampere/hour capacity.

Additional Notes on the D.C. Supply.

(1) Normally there is only one load ammeter fitted in the cockpit regardless of the number of generators. Each generator has a sensor which transmits the current flow rate to the indicator in the cockpit. The ammeter in the cockpit has a mode switch which allows the pilot to select the load indication he or she requires, i.e. select generator No.1 load or No.2 etc.

(2) The Battery Ammeter is coupled in the same way as the load ammeter.

(3) The Voltage Regulator is sometimes fitted with a Trimmer Resistor which allows fine adjustment to increase or decrease the generator output from the cockpit.

(4) A Thermistor may also be fitted to the voltage regulator to compensate for variations of resistance due to temperature changes.

(g) Load Sharing Generators
Load sharing or paralleling of generators, that is when two generators are supplying the same bus-bar, as may occur on some twin engined aircraft, requires in a D.C. supply system the voltage in each generator to be exactly, or within fine limits, the same. To achieve this the two generators are connected to each other via the voltage regulators by what is termed the equalizing circuit. Each end of the equalizing circuit is coupled to an equalizing coil in the voltage regulator which ensures the main voltage coils, which essentially control the field current, produce the same voltage in each regulator.

It should be noted, when two generators are paralleled, normally it is for safety purposes, so that in the event one generator fails the serviceable generator can provide all the requirements of the circuits. In such circumstances, should one generator fail, the voltage the other serviceable generator receives is unchanged; the load on the serviceable generator however will double.

The current at the bus-bar will remain the same as the loads and services switched on remain the same.

(h) Load Shedding
It is possible, in flight, that a generator may not produce its maximum voltage due perhaps to a minor fault, such as an accumulation of dirt on the slip rings or brushes. This may be indicated by flickering of the generator warning light, or the generator trips out in that the cut out switch opens as the battery is now providing a greater voltage than the generator, therefore the

generator warning light will remain on. Bringing the generator back on line can be achieved by reducing the load, i.e. switching off non essential services. The switching off of loads is termed load shedding.

(i) Circuit Protection

Each individual circuit will be protected against damage should a fault occur usually by one of two methods:

(1) A Fuse.

(2) A Circuit Breaker.

On some circuits both of these devices may be fitted in series with the load, normally between the switch and the load. Under normal circumstances spare fuses must be carried on the aircraft as a mandatory requirement. The pilot may replace a fuse that had blown once, should it blow a second time the engineer should be consulted. The circuit breaker must be treated in the same way as a fuse in that if it trips out it may be reset by the pilot once, then the engineer should be consulted. When a fuse is replaced, only a fuse of the same type and value should be used. Remember, fuses are rated in Amps.

(j) Re-setting Circuit Breakers

(1) Non-trip free type

As with all types of fuse and circuit breaker, they cause the circuit to be broken, or become open circuited, in the event excessive heat is generated in the conductor. The excessive heat will cause the metal wire to melt in a fuse and/or the bi-metal strip in a circuit breaker to disrupt the continuity of the conductor.

When re-setting the non-trip free circuit breaker the reset button must be pushed in and then finger pressure immediately released. It must never be held in to prevent it tripping out or the circuit may overheat and fire may result.

(2) Trip Free Circuit Breaker

This type is designed so that it cannot be inadvertently held in.

CHAPTER 3
TEST YOURSELF QUESTIONS

GENERATORS AND MOTORS

1. Fleming's Right Hand Rule is normally applied to:
    (a) generators.
    (b) motors.
    (c) magnetic fields around conductors.
    (d) transformers.

    Ref. Ch.3. Para.3.1.

2. Maximum E.M.F. is induced in the loop of an armature when the loop:
    (a) cuts the lines of magnetic flux at 90 .
    (b) cuts the lines of magnetic flux at 45 .
    (c) is moving parallel to the lines of magnetic flux.
    (d) cuts the lines of magnetic flux at 270 .

    Ref. Ch.3. Para.3.2.

3. The magnitude of the E.M.F. in a generator is dependent upon:
    (a) the size of the magnetic poles.
    (b) the number of armatures.
    (c) the strength of the magnetic field.
    (d) the cross sectional area of the conductors in the field.

    Ref. Ch.3. Para.3.4.

4. Voltage is controlled in a shunt wound D.C. generator by:
    (a) a variable resistor.
    (b) varying the R.P.M. of the generator.
    (c) a parallel variable resistor.
    (d) control of the loads or services.

    Ref. Ch.3. Para.3.10.

5. D.C generators are rated in:
    (a) KVA.
    (b) VA.
    (c) KVAR.
    (d) KW.

    Ref. Ch.3. Para.3.13.

6. In any D.C. motor:
   (a) the field is kept constant.
   (b) weakening of the field causes armature speed to increase.
   (c) weakening of the field causes armature speed to reduce.
   (d) weakening of the field will have no effect on armature speed.

   Ref. Ch.3. Para.3.18.

7. In a shunt wound motor:
   (a) the field windings are in series with the armature.
   (b) the field windings are in parallel with the motor.
   (c) the field windings are connected to an external power source.
   (d) the field windings are connected to the bus-bar.

   Ref. Ch.3. Para.3.19.

8. A shunt wound motor:
   (a) can be considered to be a constant speed machine.
   (b) has a high starting torque.
   (c) is started by connection to mains or high voltage.
   (d) is started by connection to high voltage batteries.

   Ref. Ch.3. Para.3.19.

9. To limit the current, when starting a D.C. motor:
   (a) a variable resistor is fitted in parallel with the armature.
   (b) a variable resistor is fitted in parallel with the field.
   (c) a variable resistor is fitted in series with the armature.
   (d) a variable resistor is fitted in series with the field.

   Ref. Ch.3. Para.3.22.

10. If a speed regulator is fitted to a motor, the speed switch must, before starting, be set to:
    (a) max R.P.M.
    (b) off.
    (c) min R.P.M.
    (d) disconnect.

    Ref. Ch.3. Para.3.24.

4

AIRCRAFT BATTERIES

4.1 Introduction

As has been established in previous chapters there are two primary sources of electrical energy used on modern aircraft.

(a) The generator, which converts mechanical energy into electrical energy.

(b) The battery, which converts chemical energy into electrical energy.

During normal engine operation, electrical energy is normally taken from the generator, which itself is driven by the engine. Most engines, however, are initially started with the use of electrical power, such power must be stored until required for use. The most common method employed in the storage of electrical energy is the electrical storage battery. Such batteries may also be used to provide emergency power in the event of generator failure.

Batteries may be divided into two basic types:

(a) The primary, or elementary, cell battery which generally is non-rechargeable and disposed of when all chemical energy has been used.

(b) The secondary cell battery or rechargeable type.

The majority of aircraft batteries of the rechargeable type and are of the Lead Acid or the more common Nickel Cadmium construction.

4.2 The Lead Acid Type Battery

This type of battery is very similar to those used in cars. The cells are connected in series. Each cell contains positive plates of lead peroxide, negative plates of spongy lead, and electrolyte consisting of sulphuric acid and distilled water. In discharging, the chemical energy stored in the battery is changed into electrical energy; in charging, the electrical energy supplied to the battery is changed to chemical energy and stored. It is possible to charge a storage battery many times before it deteriorates permanently.

When new the battery is initially charged from an electrical supply before the battery is fitted to the aircraft. Under normal operational conditions energy is used from the battery to provide electrical power for pre-start checks and to physically start the engine. After the engine has started, the generator, besides providing power to the various systems, will also provide power to recharge the battery to ensure it is fully charged ready for the next time its electrical supply is required.

4.3 Lead Acid Battery Construction

Figure 4-1 shows an example of the basic construction of a lead acid type battery. Each plate consists of a framework which is called a grid, and is made from lead and antimony, to which the active material (spongy lead, or lead peroxide) is attached. The positive and negative plates, item (1) on Figure 4-1, are so assembled that each positive plate is between two negative plates. Therefore the end plate in each cell is a negative plate. Between the plates are porous separators (7) which keep the positive and negative plates from touching each other and shorting out the cell. The separators have vertical ribs on the sides facing the positive plates. This construction permits the electrolyte to circulate freely around the plates. In addition, it provides a path for sediment to settle to the bottom of the cell.

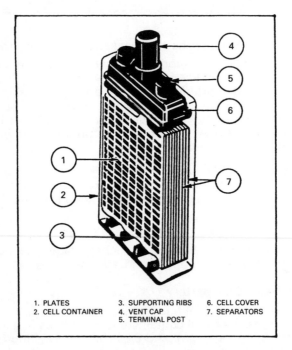

1. PLATES	3. SUPPORTING RIBS	6. CELL COVER
2. CELL CONTAINER	4. VENT CAP	7. SEPARATORS
	5. TERMINAL POST	

Fig.4-1. Lead-acid cell.

Each cell is sealed in a hard rubber casing through the top of which are terminal posts and a hole into which is fitted a nonspill type vent valve, or cap, see item (4). The hole provides access for testing the strength of the electrolyte and adding, or topping up with distilled water. The vent plug permits gases to escape from the cell with a minimum leakage of electrolyte, regardless of the position of the aircraft in flight or on the ground. Figure 4-2 shows the construction of the vent plug. In level flight, the lead weight permits venting of gases through a small hole. In inverted flight, this hole is covered by the lead weight. Vent ducts are normally provided to remove such gases that may vent from the battery directing them to atmosphere.

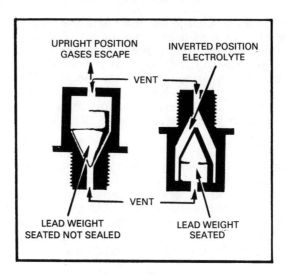

Fig.4-2. Nonspill battery vent plug.

The individual cells of the battery are connected in series by means of cell straps, as shown in Figure 4-3. The complete assembly is enclosed in an acid resistant metal container, termed the battery box, or compartment, which serves as electrical shielding and provides mechanical protection. The battery box has a removable top and also has a vent tube connection at each end. When the battery box is installed in the aircraft, a vent tube is attached to each vent tube connection. One tube is the intake tube and is exposed to the slipstream, the other is the exhaust vent tube and is attached to the battery drain sump, which is a glass jar containing a felt pad moistened with a concentration of sodium bicarbonate in solution. With this arrangement, the airstream is directed through the battery compartment, or box, where the gases are picked up, neutralized in the sump, and then expelled overboard without damage to the aircraft.

4.4   Lead Acid Type Battery Ratings

The voltage of a battery is determined by the number of cells connected in series to form the battery. Although the voltage of a single cell, when just removed from a battery charger is approximately 2.2 volts, a lead acid cell is normally rated at only 2 volts, because it soon drops to that level after removal from the charge supply. A battery rated at 12 volts consists of six cells connected in series, and a battery rated at 24 volts is composed of twelve cells.

The capacity of an aircraft storage battery is rated in ampere hours (amperes furnished by the battery times the amount of time current can be drawn). This rating indicates how long the battery may be used at a given rate before it becomes completely discharged.

Theoretically, a 100 ampere-hour battery will furnish 100 amperes for one hour, 50 amperes for two hours, or 20 amperes for five hours. Actually, the ampere output of a particular battery depends on the rate of discharge. Heavy discharge current heats the battery and decreases its efficiency and total ampere hour output. For aircraft batteries, a period of ten hours has been established as the discharge time rating battery capacity. However, this time of ten hours is only a basis for rating and does not necessarily mean the length of time during which the battery is expected to furnish current. Under actual service conditions it is possible a battery may completely discharge in a matter of minutes, or it may never discharge if the generator provides sufficient charge.

The ampere hour capacity of a battery is dependent upon its total effective plate area. Connecting batteries in parallel will increase their ampere-hour capacity and connecting batteries in series increases the total voltage but not the ampere-hour capacity. In multi engined aircraft where more than one battery is used, the batteries are usually connected in parallel. The voltage is equal to that of one battery, but the ampere-hour capacity is increased. The total capacity is the sum of the ampere-hour ratings for the individual batteries.

4.5 Factors affecting Lead Acid Battery Life

Various factors cause deterioration of a battery and shorten its service life. These include over-discharging, which causes excessive sulphation and too rapid charging or discharging, resulting in overheating of the plates and shedding of active material. The accumulation of shedded material, in turn, causes shorting of the plates and results in internal discharge. A battery that remains in a low or discharged condition for a long period of time may be permanently damaged. In addition to causing deterioration of the battery, these factors also decrease battery capacity.

4.6 Operation of Lead Acid Cells

A lead acid cell contains positive plates coated with lead peroxide (Pbo_2); negative plates made of lead (Pb); and liquid electrolyte, consisting of sulphuric acid (SO_4) and water (H_2O). During discharge, lead sulphate ($PbSO_4$) is formed on both the positive and negative plates, the acid content of the electrolyte is decreased, and its water content is increased. As discharge continues, the amount of lead sulphate on the plates increases until the sulphate coatings become so thick that the weakened electrolyte cannot effectively reach the active materials (lead and lead peroxide). When this happens, chemical reaction is retarded and the output of the cell reduced. In practice, the cell is not permitted to be discharged to this extent because thick coatings of lead peroxide are difficult to remove in charging. Additionally, a cell approaching a state of total discharge is of little use because the high internal resistance caused by the coatings of sulphate on its plates reduces the current to a value too low for practical use.

When a cell is being charged, lead sulphate is removed from both the positive and negative plates, and sulphuric acid is again formed. In the process, the water content of the electrolyte is decreased and the density of the electrolyte is increased. The open circuit voltage of a lead acid cell, that is, its voltage when there is no load drawing current, is approximately 2.2 volts.

This voltage is the same for every lead acid cell regardless of its plate size and remains at this value until the cell is practically dead, regardless of its state of discharge. When the cell approaches total discharge, its voltage begins to drop rapidly.

The closed circuit voltage of a cell, that is, its voltage under load, decreases gradually as the cell is discharged. This gradual decrease in terminal voltage is due to a gradual increase in the internal resistance of the cell caused by the sulphation of the plates. At the end of normal discharge, the internal resistance of a lead acid cell is more than twice as high as it is when fully charged. The difference between the open circuit and closed circuit terminal voltages is due to the voltage drop inside the cell. This is equal to the current the load draws multiplied by the internal resistance in the cell. Therefore, the discharging voltage that a lead acid cell can supply under closed circuit conditions is equal to the open circuit voltage of the cell minus the internal resistance drop in the cell.

To give a high discharge current and a high terminal voltage under load, a battery must have low internal resistance. This characteristic can be achieved through extensive plate area. Therefore, each cell contains several sets of plates. All the positive plates of a cell are connected by one connecting bar, and all the negative plates by another. Thus, the plates are connected in parallel, further decreasing the internal resistance of the cell. The open circuit cell voltage is not affected; it remains the same as that of a single pair of plates.

4.7 Lead Acid Battery Testing Methods

The state of charge of a storage battery depends upon the condition of its active materials, primarily the plates. However, the state of charge of a battery is indicated by the density of the electrolyte and is checked by a hydrometer, an instrument which measures the specific gravity (weight as compared with water) of liquids.

The hydrometer most commonly used consists of a small sealed glass tube weighted at its lower end so it will float upright. Within the narrow stem of the tube is a printed scale with a range of 1.100 to 1.300. The depth to which the hydrometer sinks in the electrolyte is determined by the density of the electrolyte, and the scale value indicated at the level of the electrolyte is its specific gravity. The more dense the electrolyte, the higher the hydrometer will float; therefore, the highest number on the scale (1.300) is at the lower end of the hydrometer scale. In a new, fully charged aircraft storage battery, the electrolyte is approximately 30 percent sulphuric acid and 70 percent distilled water (by volume) and is 1.300 times as heavy as pure water.

During discharge, the solution (electrolyte) becomes less dense and its specific gravity drops below 1.300. Specific gravity readings between 1.300 and 1.275 indicates a high state of charge, a medium state of charge would be between 1.275 and 1.240, and a low state of charge between 1.240 and 1.200.

Aircraft batteries are generally of small capacity but are subject to heavy loads. The values specified for state of charge are therefore rather high. Hydrometer tests are made periodically on all storage batteries installed in aircraft. An aircraft battery in a low state of charge may have perhaps 50 percent charge remaining, but is never the less low in the face of heavy demands which would soon exhaust it. A battery in such a state of charge is considered in need of immediate recharging. Aircraft batteries are given a serviceability check every three months and must achieve a minimum rate of efficiency of 80 percent. The state of charge of an aircraft battery must be checked every three months and in general before each flight.

When a battery is tested for serviceability using a hydrometer the temperature of the electrolyte must be taken into consideration. The specific gravity readings on the hydrometer will vary from the actual specific gravity as the temperature changes. No correction is necessary when the temperature is between 70°F and 90°F since the variation is not great enough to be considered. When temperatures are greater than 90°F or less than 70°F. it is necessary to apply a correction factor. Most hydrometers are supplied with a correction chart, or scale, provided.

The specific gravity of a cell is reliable only if nothing has been added to the electrolyte except occasional small amounts of distilled water to replace that lost as a result of normal evaporation. Hydrometer readings should always be taken before adding distilled water, never after. This is necessary to allow more time for the water to mix thoroughly with the electrolyte and to avoid drawing up into the syringe a sample which does not represent the true strength of the solution.

Extreme care should be exercised when making the hydrometer test of a lead acid battery cell. The electrolyte should be handled very carefully, for sulphuric acid will burn clothes and skin. If the acid does come into contact with the skin the area should be treated by a thorough washing with clean water and the area treated with bicarbonate of soda.

Care should also be taken to avoid spillage of electrolyte and, or, acid onto aircraft structure as severe corrosion to the affected area may result if the area is not treated immediately after the spillage.

4.8   Lead Acid Battery Charging Methods

A storage battery may be charged by passing direct current through the battery in a direction opposite to that of the discharge current. Because of the internal resistance in the battery, the voltage of the external charging source must be greater than the open circuit voltage. For example, the open circuit voltage of a fully charged battery, 12 cell lead acid type, is approximately 26.4 volts (12×2.2 volts), but approximately 28 volts are required to charge it. This larger voltage is required for charging because of the voltage drop in the battery caused by the internal resistance. Hence, the charging voltage of a lead acid battery must equal the open circuit voltage plus the internal resistance drop within the battery.

Batteries are charged by either the constant voltage or constant current method. In the constant voltage method, a motor generator set with a constant regulated voltage forces the current through the battery. In this method, the current at the start of the process is high but automatically tapers off, reaching the value of approximately one ampere when the battery is fully charged. The constant voltage method requires less time and supervision than does the constant current method.

In the constant current method, the current remains almost constant during the entire charging process.

This method requires a longer time to charge a battery fully and, towards the end of the charging process, presents the danger of being overcharged if care is not exercised.

In the aircraft, the storage battery is charged by direct current from the aircraft generator system. This method of charging is the constant voltage method, since the generator voltage is held constant by use of a voltage regulator.

When a storage battery is being charged, it generates a certain amount of hydrogen and oxygen. Since this is an explosive mixture, it is important that measures are taken to prevent ignition of the gas mixture. During the charging process the vent caps should be loosened and left in place. No open flames, sparks, or other sources of ignition should be permitted in the vicinity. Before connecting or disconnecting a battery to be charged, always turn off the power at the main supply source.

Note:
The action of loosening vent caps during charging only applies to batteries being charged in a servicing bay situation and not when the battery is being charged by normal process in the aircraft.

4.9 Nickel Cadmium Batteries

The primary advantages of the Nickel Cadmium Battery, usually referred to as the Ni-cad battery, are its low maintenance cost, excellent reliability, good starting capability, and a short recharge time coupled with a long life.

4.10 Nickel Cadmium Cell Construction

As in the lead acid type battery, the cell is the basic unit of the ni-cad battery. It consists of positive and negative plates, separators, electrolyte, cell vent and cell container. The positive plates are made from a porous plaque on which nickel hydroxide has been deposited. In both cases the porous plaque is obtained by sintering nickel powder to a fine wire mesh screen. Sintering is a process which fuses together extemely small granules of powder at a high temperature. After the active positive and negative materials are deposited on the plaque, it is formed and cut into the proper plate size. A nickel tab is then welded to a corner of each plate and the plates are assembled with the tabs welded to the proper terminals. The plates are separated from each other by a continuous strip of porous plastic. The electrolyte used in the ni-cad battery is 30 percent solution (by weight) of potassium hydroxide (KOH) in distilled water. The specific gravity of the electrolyte remains between 1.240 and 1.300 at room temperature. No appreciable changes occur in the electrolyte during charge or discharge, as a result, the battery state of charge cannot be determined by a specific gravity check of the electrolyte using a normal hydrometer. The electrolyte level should be maintained just above the level of the plates.

4.11   Operation of Nickel Cadmium Cells

When a charging current is applied to a ni-cad battery, the negative plates lose oxygen and begin forming metallic cadmium. The active material of the positive plates, nickel hydroxide, becomes more highly oxidized. This process continues while the charging current is applied, or until all the oxygen is removed from the negative plates and only cadmium remains. Towards the end of the charging cycle the cells emit gas. This will also occur if the cells are over-charged. This gas is caused by decomposition of water in the electrolyte into hydrogen at the negative plates and oxygen at the positive plates. The voltage used during charging, as well as the temperature, determines when gassing will occur. To completely charge a nickel cadmium battery, some gassing, however slight, must take place; thus some water will be used.

The chemical action is reversed when discharging takes place. The positive plates slowly give up oxygen, which is regained by the negative plates. This process results in the conversion of the chemical energy into electrical energy. During discharge the plates absorb a quantity of the electrolyte. On recharge the level of the electrolyte rises and, at full charge the electrolyte will be at its highest level. Therefore distilled water should only be added when the battery is fully charged.

4.12   Precautions to Note with Ni-cad Batteries

For servicing purposes, a separate storage and maintenance area should be provided for nickel cadmium batteries. The electrolyte is chemically opposite to the sulphuric acid used in a lead acid battery. Fumes from a lead acid battery can contaminate the electrolyte of a ni-cad battery.

This precaution of keeping the two types completely separate should be extended to equipment, tools and syringes. Acid must not be allowed near a ni-cad battery.

The potassium hydroxide electrolyte used in ni-cad batteries is extremely corrosive. When handling the electrolyte protective goggles, gloves and rubber aprons should be used. Suitable washing facilities should be provided in case the electrolyte is spilt on clothing or skin. Such exposures should be rinsed immediately with clean water or a boric acid solution. In an emergency vinegar or lemon juice may be used.

4.13   State of Charge and Charging

Since the electrolyte does not react chemically with the cell plates, the specific gravity of the electrolyte does not change appreciably. Therefore, it is not possible to determine the state of charge of the battery with a hydrometer; nor can the charge be determined by a voltage test because the voltage of a ni-cad battery remains constant during 90 percent of the discharge cycle.

Charging can be accomplished by either the constant voltage or constant current method. For constant potential charging, maintain the charging voltage constant until the charging current decays to 3 amperes or less ensuring that the battery cell temperature does not exceed 100°F. For constant current charging, start the charge and continue until the voltage reaches the desired potential; reduce the current level to 4 amps; continue charging until the desired voltage, or until the battery exceeds 100°F and the voltage begins to decline.

4.14 Thermal Runaway

Normally batteries are able to perform to their rated capacities when temperature and the charging rates are within their specified values. Should these values be exceeded, however, a condition known as thermal runaway can occur.

When this happens, there will be violent gassing, the electrolyte will boil, and damage will occur to the battery case and plates through melting. All of this may also result in damage to the aircraft structure and the electrical system.

Batteries generally have a low thermal capacity and this results in rapid heat dissipation which in turn causes internal resistance to decrease. When being charged, therefore, a lower resistance will allow a greater charge rate, higher temperature still, and the runaway condition is achieved. Some aircraft, in particular those which use nickel cadmium batteries, have temperature sensing devices located to warn the pilot of a pending runaway condition. In some systems the battery is automatically isolated, in others the battery must be isolated manually.

CHAPTER 4
TEST YOURSELF QUESTIONS
BATTERIES

1. As a lead acid battery is taken off charge, the maximum state of charge in an individual cell will be:
    (a) 2.0V.
    (b) 12.0V.
    (c) 12.2V.
    (d) 2.2V.

    Ref. Ch.4. Para.4.4.

2. A one hundred ampere/hour battery will furnish 50 Amps for:
    (a) 1 Hour.
    (b) 30 Minutes.
    (c) 2 Hours.
    (d) 50 Hours.

    Ref. Ch.4. Para.4.4.

3. The electrolyte of a lead acid battery is:
    (a) Sulphuric acid and water.
    (b) Hydrochloric acid and distilled water.
    (c) Sulphuric acid and distilled water.
    (d) Potassium hydroxide and distilled water.

    Ref. Ch.4. Para.4.4.

4. The acid content of the electrolyte in a lead acid battery is:
    (a) 70% by weight.
    (b) 30% by volume.
    (c) 30% by weight.
    (d) 70% by volume.

    Ref. Ch.4. Para.4.4.

5. If the electrolyte of a Ni-cad battery is spilt on the skin:
    (a) it can be considered harmless.
    (b) the area should be treated with boric acid.
    (c) the area should be treated with sodium bicarbonate.
    (d) the area should be treated with potassium hydroxide.

    Ref. Ch.4. Para.4.12.

5

BASIC ELECTRICAL COMPONENTS

5.1 Introduction

The basis of an electrical circuit is the item of equipment, usually termed the 'load', and the cable connecting it to the electrical supply, but in practice such simplicity is rarely encountered as it may be necessary to provide a means of stopping and starting the flow of current (switch), controlling the amount of current flowing (rheostat), safeguarding the circuit from damage by excessive current (fuse), while it is also advantageous to provide points at which a number of cables can be connected together (terminal or plug). Simple components that fulfil the requirements mentioned, are as follows.

5.2 Cable

The electric current necessary to operate electrical equipment is conveyed from a source of supply, i.e., generator or battery, by means of a conductor. To confine the current to its proper path, it is necessary to sheath the conductors with an insulating material. Such a sheathed conductor is termed an electric cable. A conductor which is sheathed only with enamel or fibre (silk, cotton, or rayon) is not classed as cable, but as 'insulated wire'.

A cable consists of one or more sheathed conductors, known as cores, and an outer protective covering. The conductor of each core is usually made of a number of strands of tinned copper wire, although other metals, such as aluminium and steel are occasionally used for special purposes. To facilitate circuit tracing and fault location, the insulation of each core of multi-core cable is appropriately coloured.

The number of strands and the gauge of the wire of a cable depend on its current-carrying capacity and the degree of flexibility required. Therefore, when renewing a cable, the replacement cable must be of similar specification to that removed, otherwise serious damage to the cable may occur.

The outer covering of the cable which binds the cores together, is primarily protective, and the materials used for it are chosen with a view to the conditions under which the cable will be used. Among the materials employed are cellulose, cotton braiding treated with varnish, tough rubber, plastic (polyvinyl chloride — P.V.C.), copper wire braiding, and lead sheathing.

(a) Fitting

The following are general points that are observed when fitting cables:

(1) When stripping back the outer covering to expose the cores, the insulation of the cores must not be cut or damaged.

(2) When stripping back the core insulation to prepare the wire for connection, cutting of the wire strands must be avoided; the strands must not be cut to facilitate fitting a connector. Every strand must be in circuit when the cable is connected.

(3) Where a cable connector is not used, the core strands must be twisted together and looped under the washer of the terminal screw in a clockwise direction. This will ensure that tightening the screw does not tend to unhook the wire.

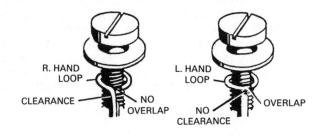

Fig.5-1. Direct screw connection.

(4) If a connector is to be soldered to a cable, resin must be used as a flux. All other fluxes are corrosive and are not permitted for electrical work; a special wire type solder with a resin core is usually used.

(5) When installed, cables should be supported throughout their length without undue slackness. Supporting clips and cleats must be lined with insulating material to protect the cables from chafing.

(b) Faults

Electrical failures in simple circuits are attributable to one or more of four main causes. i.e., short-circuits, insulation failure, loss of continuity, and incorrect connection of cables.

(1) Short-circuits

Can be regarded as an abnormal decrease of resistance, causing excessive current to flow; this results in overheating, blowing of fuses, and possibly damage to insulation. They can be caused by breakdown of insulation, loose strands of wire between adjacent cable ends and terminals, metal swarf or metallic dirt collecting between 'live' portions of equipment, or by mechanical damage to cables or components.

(2) Insulation Failure
Can be caused by hydraulic fluid, oil, grease, gasoline, kerosine, dampness, etc., chemical action, chafing or abrasion of cables, and overheating of conductors due to excessive current.

(3) Loss of Continuity
Can be regarded as an abnormal increase of resistance in the circuit, restricting or stopping the flow of current. Can be caused by partial breakage of the conductor, e.g., when several strands of a flexible conductor are broken at the cable end, by badly soldered joints, by loose terminals, or by dirty or uneven contact surfaces.

Note:
Badly soldered joints are usually referred to as 'dry' joints.

(4) Incorrect Connection of Cables
This class of fault has its origin in bad workmanship; it should never occur in a circuit which is installed or serviced by a competent mechanic. This fault is certain to cause either non-operation or inefficient operation of the circuit; it may easily cause serious damage to cables or equipment by short-circuit faults.

Note:
Faults in electrical equipment observed by an airframe mechanic must be reported immediately to the electrical tradesman.

5.3 Switches

Switches are used to complete or interrupt a circuit, thereby starting or stopping the flow of current to the load. The simplest form of switch consists of two contacts which are insulated from each other, one connected to the supply, the other to the load, the gap between the two contacts being bridged when required by a movable metallic unit.

The movable unit, or 'movement', is generally spring loaded to ensure good contact and a quick opening action, both of which are necessary if sparking at the contacts is to be avoided. Most switches are operated by moving a knob or 'dolly', but rotary switches in which the handle is twisted are often used when it is necessary to guard against accidental operation.

Note:
Before operating any switch, ensure that the service affected is known.

Switches have an important function to perform; the following are general points that are observed for their efficient operation:

(a) Examined frequently for signs of mechanical wear or damage by burning.

(b) Contact surfaces are kept clean and free from all traces of pitting, burning or corrosion.

(c) A switch which becomes erratic in its action (a fault caused by wear in the movement, or its pivots) is renewed immediately.

5.4 Fuses

Fuses are safety devices which are placed in circuits to protect them from excessive currents. If a circuit carries current in excess of that for which it was designed, the components of the circuit will become overheated. Such overheating may cause damage and fire.

A fuse usually consists of a short strand of wire which is positioned in a circuit so that all the current passes through it. If the current becomes excessive, the heat generated in the fuse will melt it and prevent the passage of further current. The current at which the fuse melts depends on the diameter of the wire and the material of which it is made.

Fig.5-2. Types of aircraft fuse.

A blowing fuse produces a spark, and to avoid the risk of fire or explosion, which might occur if gasoline fumes are present, aircraft fuses are totally enclosed in glass tubes fitted with brass end caps. Stamped on the end cap is the value of permissible current allowed to flow. The fuse fits into two contact clips in a fuse box; terminal screws at the base of the clips serve to connect the fuse with the circuit.

The following points are noted when checking or renewing fuses:

(a) A blown fuse indicates a fault in the circuit; the fuse may be replaced by the pilot ONCE, if it blows again, the engineer must be consulted.

(b) Care must be taken to ensure that replacement fuses are of the same value as those removed. Because it is dangerous, it is strictly forbidden to replace a blown fuse by one of higher rating.

(c) Fuses are inspected periodically and renewed if the wire shows signs of sagging or discolouration.

5.5 Rheostats

The rate of flow of current in a circuit is dependent on the voltage applied to the circuit and upon its resistance. Normally, the voltage applied is constant, and any variation of current must be obtained by varying the resistance of the circuit. Rheostats, which are simply variable resistances, are used for this purpose.

Most rheostats consist of a length of high-resistance wire wound on a former, with a sliding contact which varies the effective length of resistance wire in the circuit. The rheostat has two terminals, one connected to one end of the resistance wire, and the other to the sliding contact or, in some instances, to the contact and to the end of the wire.

Dimmer Switch

Many rheostats used in lighting circuits to control the brilliancy of the lamps, are so designed that the sliding contact can be moved beyond the end of the resistance wire, thus breaking the circuit. This arrangement, which is in effect a combination of switch and rheostat, is utilised in dimmer switches which are often used on aircraft instrument panels.

5.6 Relay Switches

The switches mentioned in the previous paragraphs are all of the direct-operating type, but for many purposes it is advantageous to use switches that can be remotely controlled. These switches, known as relay switches, are operated by an electro-magnet, comprising a solenoid and soft iron armature connected to a separate electrical control circuit.

Relay switches can be regarded as belonging to one or other of two groups, e.g., heavy duty or control relays. The former are often used in heavy-current starter motor circuits, while control relays form an essential part of many automatic control systems.

(a) Heavy Duty Relay

The main problem when operating large motors on low-voltage systems is one of voltage drop in the supply cables, due to the large current involved. The use of a remotely controlled switch permits the cables to be run directly from the supply to the motor; by reducing the length of cable, the voltage drop is correspondingly reduced.

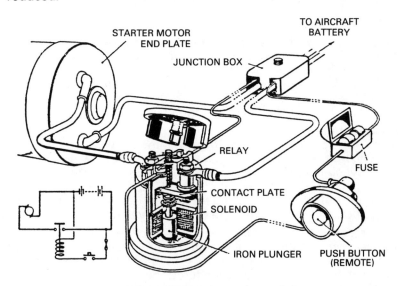

Fig.5-3. Heavy duty relay switch.

The illustration shows a starter motor circuit using a heavy duty relay. When the control push-button is pressed, a current flows through the solenoid to energise the electro-magnet. The plunger (armature) is drawn into the hollow core of the solenoid, causing the heavy copper contact-plate to bridge the two fixed contacts and thus complete the circuit to the motor.

When the control push-button is released, the electro-magnet is de-energised. The spring is then able to return the armature and contact plate to their original position, thus interrupting the circuit to the motor.

(b) Control Relay

These relays operate on the same principle as the heavy-duty type, i.e., by electro-magnet, but their contact assembly is of light construction, since the current to be handled by the contacts is relatively small. The solenoid winding is generally of high resistance enabling the relay to be energised continuously, if required, without overheating.

Many variations of contact assembly are in use, ranging from single-pole switch-action to four-pole action. For example, in the fire extinguishing circuit the relay may control four circuits, the contacts being either opened or closed on energising the magnet. Relays having a selector-switch action, i.e., opening one circuit and closing another when energised are often used for control of electro-hydraulic valves, etc.

Note:

Although a solenoid and armature are used in both relays and valves, the armature in the relay operates contacts, and the armature in the valve operates the valve element.

5.7 Filament Lamps

A piece of metal which is heated to a bright red will not only radiate heat, but it will also emit a certain amount of light. This property of light-emission due to temperature is termed incandescence. As stated, an electric current passing through a conductor has a heating effect; if this effect is great enough, the conductor will become incandescent and give off light. This is the principle of the filament lamp.

(a) Construction

The lamp consists of a thin thread (filament) of wire, usually made of tungsten, enclosed in a glass envelope from which all air has been evacuated. The glass envelope is necessary, otherwise oxygen contained in the atmosphere would combine with the heated filament, which would disintegrate almost immediately. Lamps constructed in this manner are known as vacuum lamps.

Tungsten melts at 3,400°C, but in a vacuum evaporation of the metal, which causes blackening of the glass envelope with a reduction in light-emission, sets in at 2,000°C. To enable the filament to be worked at high temperatures, thus increasing the efficiency of the lamp, the glass envelope may be filled with an inert gas, i.e., argon or nitrogen — gas which will not combine with other elements. These types of lamp are termed gas-filled, and have a light-output per watt approximately double that of a corresponding vacuum lamp.

(b) Classification

Filament lamps are classified according to the voltage of the supply for which they are designed, and their rate of consumption in watts. To describe a lamp in terms of voltage alone is inadequate; 24 volt lamps range from small indicator lamps of 3 watts consumption to large searchlight lamps taking 900 watts. Wattage alone is likewise insufficient; the description must include both terms, e.g., 24 volts, 6 watts; 230 volts, 100 watts.

A further classification point is the type of end cap fitted to the lamp, through which electrical connection is made to the filament. The diameter of the end cap is measured in millimetres. The most common types of cap are as follows:

(1) Edison Screw Cap

These are centre-contact caps of the form shown in the illustration, the metal screw portion forming one contact. The large contact area makes this cap suitable for heavy-current lamps, while the certainty of alignment of contacts is an added advantage.

(2) Bayonet Cap

This is the most common type of cap met with in British lamps. It may be either a centre contact, double contact or treble contact; its chief advantage is the ease with which it can be inserted and withdrawn from the lamp-holder.

(3) Pre-focus Cap

This cap is used in light fittings where focus is important and must be pre-set by the manufacturer, rather than by local adjustment. Typical uses are in searchlights, landing lamps, signalling lamps, etc.

PRE-FOCUS   EDISON SCREW   BAYONET

Fig.5-4. Types of lamp cap.

5.8 Bonding

During flight a static electrical charge is induced into metallic parts of an aircraft, and any intermittent contact between parts of different potential may cause sparking with consequent risk of fire; sparking also interferes with radio reception.

To prevent these hazards, and to provide a large constant-capacity earth to increase radio efficiency, every metal component of an aircraft is bonded (electrically-interconnected) so that the potential throughout the aircraft structure is uniform. Wooden and composite aircraft have earth strips of tinned copper, extending along the main components and connected to a common earth terminal; each metal component being bonded to the copper strip by means of a bonding lead of braided flexible copper wire. All-metal aircraft are bonded satisfactorily without the use of an earth strip as the airframe structure is used for this purpose.

To obtain continuity throughout the aircraft, bonding leads, strips of brass or copper, or copper gauze are connected to or interposed between metal components, though with clean metal-to-metal joints additional contact is not necessary. Component parts that are removable from the aircraft are provided with bonding terminals to which the bonding lead is connected.

Note:
Before removing an airframe component, ensure that the bonding has been disconnected, and after fitting a component, ensure that the bonding is reconnected.

Electrical Conducting Tyres
When the aircraft lands, induced static electricity would tend to pass from the aircraft to the earth and cause a spark. To prevent this happening, aircraft nose and tail wheel tyres are specially constructed of rubber composition of low resistance, thus providing a path to earth for the static electricity.

ELECTRICAL SUPPLY IN AIRCRAFT

5.9 Introduction

Certain items in aircraft, such as radio and radar equipment, lighting equipment, and many types of aircraft instrument depend entirely for their operation on a suitable electrical supply.

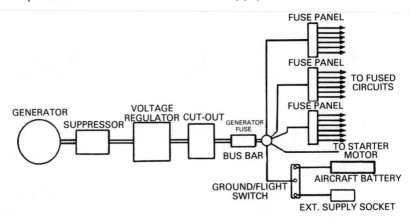

Fig.5-5. Single generator installation.

Remote control and operation of other items can be accomplished much more simply by electrical means than by manual, hydraulic or pneumatic methods. Furthermore, most safety devices, and almost all automatically-controlled equipment are dependent wholly, or in part, on electricity for their operation.

Electric cables are more flexible, less bulky, less vulnerable, and much easier to repair or renew than are hydraulic or pneumatic pipelines, or flexible mechanical drives. Other advantages in the use of electrical equipment include the following:

(a) Cleanliness.

(b) Lightness and compactness of electrical components; saving in weight and space.

(c) Electrical components supersede complicated linkages.

(d) Quicker response of components.

(e) Pressurization efficiency increased.

5.10 Suppressor

As stated, the main electrical supply in aircraft is provided by one or more D.C. generators driven, through gearing, by the aero-engines; an emergency supply, available in the event of generator failure is provided by a battery.

Sparking at the brushes of a generator results in the radiation of electro-magnetic waves, which interfere with radio reception. Such radiation may take place not only from the generator, but also from any circuit connected to it. The interference may also be conducted along the wiring to the power unit of the radio equipment, if this is supplied from the general distribution point (bus-bar).

Prevention of radio interference is achieved in two stages. The generator is totally enclosed in a metallic casing, and the supply cables from the generator are either sheathed with metal braid or are enclosed in a metal conduit (sleeve); this prevents direct radiation. To prevent interference being conducted along the wiring, suppressors are fitted to the ends of the 'screened' cables as close to the generator as is possible.

5.11 Voltage Regulator

The voltage supplied by the generator must remain constant if the electrical equipment is to operate with maximum efficiency. Since the generator speed is directly proportional to the speed of the aero-engine, some form of automatic voltage control is necessary; this is achieved by the use of a voltage regulator.

With the use of a voltage regulator, the output voltage of a shunt-wound D.C. generator can be regulated by automatic control of the field current. If, for example, the voltage rises because of increased speed or decreased load, the field current is reduced accordingly.

Voltage control is usually obtained through a voltage regulator in which a pile of carbon washers, held together by spring pressure, is connected in series with the generator field winding. Any fluctuation of voltage varies the spring pressure, thereby varying the resistance of the field and adjusting the field current to cancel out voltage variation.

5.12 Cut-out

The aircraft battery is intended to supply current in the event of generator failure, and must therefore be connected to the distribution bus-bar at all times, unless the whole installation is out of service or an external supply is being applied to the bus-bar. Under normal operating conditions, with the generator output voltage at its correct level, the battery takes a small charging current, and the entire load is supplied by the generator.

In the event of the generator voltage falling below the battery voltage, the entire load will fall on the battery, and the generator will take a reverse current which, because of the low resistance of the generator armature would be quite heavy and cause damage to the armature windings and discharge of the battery.

It is, therefore, essential that the generator is not connected to the bus-bar until the generator voltage exceeds the battery voltage, and that the generator should be disconnected from the bus-bar whenever a sizable reverse current begins to flow through its windings. These functions are done, automatically, by the cut-out. In this case the cut-out switch will open when generator output falls ½ volt below battery output.

5.13 Distribution

All aircraft loads, with the exception of starter motors, are supplied through protective devices. Simple fuses of suitable rating are used for the smaller load circuits; the fuses are generally grouped in covered fuseboxes or on covered panels supplied from the distribution bus-bar. Large circuits are often fed through thermal circuit breakers; these replace the normal type of fuse and consist of a special switch which opens automatically if unduly heavy current is carried; they can be re-set by hand or electrically, after the circuit fault has been rectified.

Most modern aircraft are wired on the 'single-pole' system. In this system, one terminal (usually the negative) of the battery, generator and each item of electrical equipment is connected to the metal of the airframe at selected 'earthing' points. A saving of cable results from this method, as the return path of the current is through the metal of the airframe, also fault location is simplified.

The distribution of electric current to all electric components of an aircraft is arranged, via cables, as follows:

(a) Bus-bars
These are the main points receiving electric current from generator and battery.

(b) Distribution Panels
These incorporate or are connected to a bus-bar, and provide electric current to separate circuits. They usually contain fuses. Distribution panels must be fitted with covers; any covers missing must be reported to the electrical tradesman.

(c) Conduits
These contain the cables, thus providing protection and facilitating cable grouping. Damaged conduits must be reported to the electrical tradesman.

(d) Plugs and Sockets
These are used at all points where frequent disconnection is

necessary, e.g., wing roots, portable electric components, etc. They also assist in efficient pressurisation of the aircraft, e.g., bulkheads, etc. Before removing any airframe component, ensure that plugs and sockets are not fitted. If fitted, the plug and socket must be disconnected by the electrical tradesman.

(e) Terminal Block
    These provide a simple means of connecting cables, but wherever possible are replaced by plugs and sockets.

5.14 External Supplies

When servicing and testing the electrical equipment of aircraft prior to flight, and when starting aircraft fitted with electric starters the current demand is extremely heavy. The capacity of the aircraft battery is insufficient to meet these demands, and an independent external supply is connected to the aircraft installation.

The external supply is obtained from batteries, or an engine-driven generator, mounted on a wheeled truck, termed an electric servicing trolley or ground power unit. This supply unit is connected to the aircraft external supply socket by a heavy cable and a plug. To isolate the aircraft battery from the bus-bars when the external supply is connected, a switch, termed a ground/flight switch may be fitted in the circuit. When this switch is set to 'Ground', the aircraft battery is isolated; when it is set to 'Flight' the aircraft battery is in circuit.

In modern aircraft, the ground/flight switch is replaced by a special plug on the end of the external supply cable and a special socket on the aircraft which, when engaged, automatically isolates the aircraft battery. With this type of circuit, a manually-operated battery isolating switch is usually provided in the cockpit which enables the pilot to switch off the electric current from the battery in an emergency, e.g., crash landing, thus minimising the fire risk.

Some aircraft are fitted with relays in circuit with the inertia switch, which isolates the battery automatically should the aircraft crash land.

Notes:
(1) Irrespective of the setting of the battery isolating switch or ground/flight switch, essential services such as fire extinguishing, dinghy release, etc., are not isolated as they are connected, via switches, direct to the aircraft battery.
(2) Ground power must be switched off when connecting or disconnecting to or from the aircraft.

ELECTRICAL INDICATORS

5.15 Introduction

As a means of attracting attention and conveying information to the pilot, various types of electrical indicator are situated in the cockpit.

(a) Warning Lights
    May be used to indicate fuel, oil, or cabin pressure failure, power failure, position of alighting gear, fire warning, etc.

(b) Electro-magnetic Indicators
To indicate fuel contents, oil temperature, engine speed, flap position, etc.

(c) Buzzer
This audible warning device, which warned the pilot that the alighting gear was in a retracted or unlocked position when he attempted to throttle back the engines, has been superseded on most aircraft by a warning light.

Where it is sufficient to know that a component is UP or DOWN, or a system is ON or OFF, warning lights are used. When more detailed information is required such as the amount of movement, variation in contents or pressure, electro-magnetic indicators are used, though on modern aircraft warning lights are being replaced, where possible, by electro-magnetic indicators.

5.16   Warning Lights

The warning lights consist of small filament lamps fitted behind coloured screens. Dependent on the type of circuit, the lamps may be illuminated by operation of a pressure switch, relay, micro switch, or flame detector switch.

Pressure Switch
With this type of switch, when installed to indicate pressure failure, the pressure exerted on a plunger opens the contacts and the warning light is OFF. Should the pressure fail, the plunger, assisted by a spring closes the contacts and the warning light comes ON.

Relay
The relay consists of a solenoid which, when energised, moves an armature. Dependent on the purpose of the relay, contacts operated by the armature may be closed or opened, thus initiating the warning light. As a power failure warning device, the main relay opens when the generator fails and connects the warning light relay to the battery, thus energising its solenoid which attracts an armature. Contacts operated by the armature close, and the power failure warning light is illuminated by current from the battery.

Micro Switch
The term 'micro' has no bearing on the size or current-carrying ability of

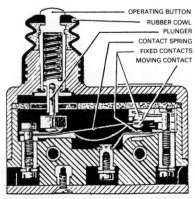

OPERATING BUTTON
RUBBER COWL
PLUNGER
CONTACT SPRING
FIXED CONTACTS
MOVING CONTACT

Fig.5-6. Micro switch.

the switch, but refers to the very short travel (.025 in. approx.) of the operating plunger. The switch consists of a spring-loaded plunger which, when depressed, causes internal switch contacts to operate with a snap action by a flat spring to which they are fitted. Any further depression of the plunger is termed 'over travel', and is taken up by the plunger spring.

One of the many uses of micro switches is to operate the alighting gear warning lights. The micro switches are situated on the airframe structure so that when the alighting gear moves, the plungers are depressed or released, and contacts initiate the warning lamps. Micro switches are also often used as external limit switches, e.g., by opening the electrical circuit when movement of an actuator has reached its allotted travel.

Flame Detector Switch

One type of flame detector switch consists of an expansion tube of alloy steel housing contacts mounted on a special spring-bow assembly. At normal temperature, the spring-bow assembly is under compression so that the springs are bowed and the contacts are open. When heat is applied, the steel tube expands to a greater extent than the spring-bow assembly; the compression is eased, the contacts close and so complete the circuit to the warning lamp.

A subsequent drop in temperature recompresses the spring-bow assembly, opens the contacts and causes the warning lamp to go out. This switch is termed a resetting type flame detector.

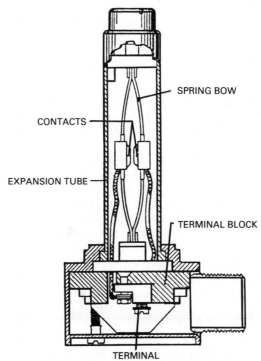

Fig.5-7. Resetting type flame detector.

5.17 Electro-magnetic Indicators

To convey measurement of position, contents or pressure to remotely situated indicators, various electrical systems of transmission are used in aircraft. The Desynn system here described, which can be adapted to indicate all these measurements, consists of an indicator and transmitter electrically connected to each other and energised by the aircraft direct current supply. When the transmitter mechanism is moved, the indicator pointer follows the movement.

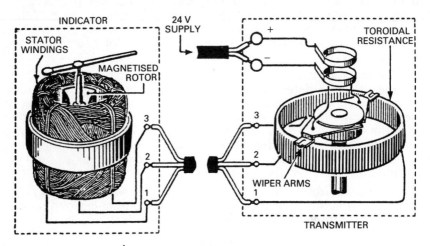

Fig.5-8. Desynn transmission system.

The transmitter consists of an endless coil of resistance wire wound on a ring-shaped former, the assembly being termed a 'toroidal resistance'. The resistance is tapped at three equidistant points, and conductors from these points lead to the indicator. A central spindle in the transmitter carries two wiper arms which bear on the toroidal resistance at points diametrically opposite. The arms are insulated from each other at the spindle, but are connected, via sliding contacts, to the electrical supply.

The indicator consists of a soft iron stator and a magnetised rotor. Disposed around the stator are three windings which, for functional purposes, may be considered as three coils placed 120 degrees apart. One end of each coil is connected to a transmitter tapping, and the remaining three ends are connected together. The rotor is a two-pole magnet mounted on a pivoted spindle at the centre of the stator; the indicating pointer is secured to the rotor spindle.

Since the wiper arms of the transmitter are connected to the power supply, current will enter the toroidal resistance at the positive arm and divide, half flowing to the negative arm in a clockwise direction and the other half flowing to it in an anti-clockwise direction. With a supply voltage of 24 volts, the progressive drop in voltage around the resistance will be indicated by the figures in the following illustrations.

Referring to Figure 5-9 the tapping to which coil 'A' is connected is at 24 volts potential, whilst coils B and C are at 8 volts respectively. Current will flow from the higher to the lower potential, i.e., in through A and out via B and C. By applying the grasp rule, it can be seen that coil A will establish a north polarity at its inner end, and coils B and C south polarities. The resultant field at the centre of the stator will hold the rotor in the position shown.

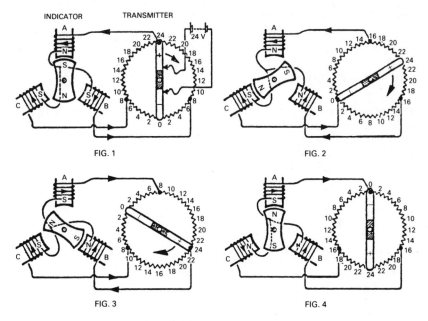

Fig.5-9. Desynn principle.

In Figure 2, the wiper arms have rotated 60 degrees clockwise. Potentials fed to the indicator coils are now, coil A — 16 volts, coil B — 16 volts, coil C — 0 volts. Current will flow in through A and B, and out through C creating north polarities at A and B and a south polarity at C. The rotor aligns itself with the field as shown; the rotor has moved through the same angle as the wiper arms. Similarly, in Figures 3 and 4 it may be seen that as the wiper arms continue to rotate, the indicator rotor will follow them.

Note:
To demonstrate the operation of the Desynn electrical indicator, 60 degree steps of the wiper arms have been used, but intermediate positions on the indicator are similarly obtained.

Position Indicators
These are used to indicate to the pilot and engineer the attitude or setting of remote movable components such as air brakes, flaps, trimming tabs, etc.

The transmitter is mounted near and coupled to the component, so that when the component is moved the transmitter spindle is rotated. The transmitter is electrically connected to an indicator in the cockpit and to the electrical supply. As the component moves, the transmitter operates the indicator which follows the movement and provides a continuous indication of the position of the component.

Note:

Should the power to the instrument fail, an 'off-scale' device consisting of a weak magnet situated near the rotor, attracts the rotor and moves it to a position where the pointer is held off the scale. The pilot will then be aware that the instrument is not working.

Electrically all transmitters are similar to that previously described, but mechanically they differ to suit the components to which they are coupled. Three types are in use, the toroidal resistance in each being housed above the drive.

(a) Direct Drive

The wiper arms of direct drive transmitters are driven directly from a central spindle in the transmitter. When the spindle is coupled with the component, an angular displacement of the component will cause a similar displacement of the wiper arms. The indicator dial is calibrated in degrees of rotation.

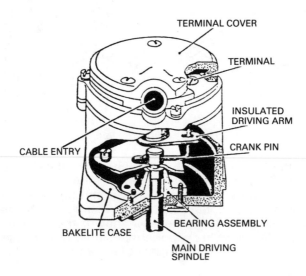

Fig.5-10. Direct drive.

(b) Radial Arm Drive

Where small angular movements are to be measured, the radial arm drive transmitter is used. It is connected to the moving component by a link which is attached to the end of the radial arm. A sector and pinion gear is built into the transmitter, so that a small displacement of the radial arm will cause a relatively larger displacement of the wiper arms. A tensioned spring is mounted on the central spindle to take up play between the gears and in the connecting linkage, so that no lost motion will occur when the direction of movement is reversed.

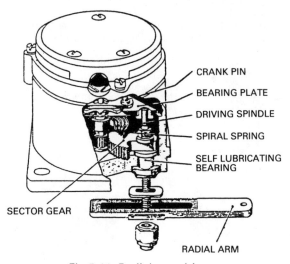

CRANK PIN

BEARING PLATE

DRIVING SPINDLE

SPIRAL SPRING

SELF LUBRICATING BEARING

SECTOR GEAR

RADIAL ARM

Fig.5-11. Radial arm drive.

(c) Push Rod Drive

The push rod drive transmitter is designed to use in conjunction with linear actuating gear. It is coupled to the moving member by a connecting rod which screws into the end of the push rod and is locked by a locknut. The push rod has a rack cut into its surface which engages with a pinion on the central spindle of the transmitter. When the push road is operated, the rack rotates the spindle which moves the wiper arms over the toroidal resistance. A tensioned spring is fitted to the spindle to prevent lost motion between the rack and pinion.

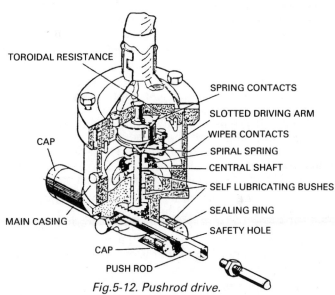

TOROIDAL RESISTANCE

SPRING CONTACTS

SLOTTED DRIVING ARM

WIPER CONTACTS

CAP

SPIRAL SPRING

CENTRAL SHAFT

SELF LUBRICATING BUSHES

SEALING RING

MAIN CASING

SAFETY HOLE

CAP

PUSH ROD

Fig.5-12. Pushrod drive.

Fuel Contents Gauge
The Desynn fuel contents gauge provides a continuous indication in gallons of the quantity of fuel in the tank of an aircraft. Where several

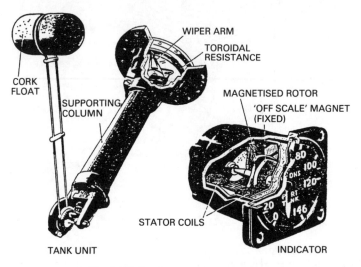

Fig.5-13. Fuel contents gauge.

fuel tanks are fitted, a separate gauge system is used for each tank. Each system comprises a tank unit and an indicator. A float on the tank unit operates a transmitter; the float responds to the level of fuel in the tank and positions the wiper arm of the transmitter accordingly. The transmitter is electrically connected to an indicator in the cockpit and to the electrical supply.

Since the fuel level is taken as a measure of the contents of the tank, the size and shape of the tank must be considered. Each tank unit and indicator is therefore designed and calibrated to suit a specific type of tank, and the appropriate tank part number is marked on both the tank unit and the indicator.

The cork float of the tank unit is attached to the end of a light steel arm, which is pivoted from a cylindrical supporting column. The arm is geared to a spindle which passes through the column to connect with a transmitter housed in a recess at the other end of the column. When the float arm rises and falls with the level of fuel in the tank, the spindle turns the wiper arms of the transmitter so that the arms always occupy a position corresponding to the fuel level. Limit stops prevent the float arm from touching the sides of the tank at the two extreme positions.

Where the mark number of a fuel gauge system is starred, e.g., Mk.4B*, it denotes that a low level warning device is fitted. This consists of a contact assembly housed in the transmitter head of the tank unit and a warning light in the cockpit. When the fuel level becomes low, contact is made by the movement of the wiper arms, and the warning lamp lights.

Pressure Gauge
The system comprises a transmitter unit and an indicator. The

transmitter is installed near the engine and connected to the pressure system by a short flexible pipe. The indicator is mounted on the instrument panel in the cockpit. The transmitter is electrically connected to the indicator and to the electrical supply.

The indicator is similar to the Desynn indicators previously described, but the transmitter unit contains a pressure sensitive device coupled to a micro-transmitter.

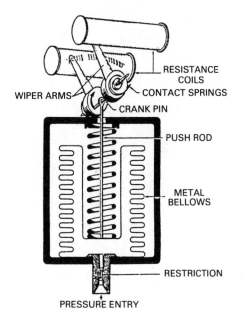

Fig.5-14. Oil pressure transmitter.

The pressure sensitive device is located in the lower part of the unit and consists of a corrugated metal bellows and a control spring. Pressure is fed into the bellows from a union at the bottom of the transmitter, and the bellows expand against the thrust of the spring. Movement of the bellows is conveyed to the micro-transmitter by a push rod. To prevent pump pulsations affecting the bellows, the bore of the inlet union is restricted.

The micro-transmitter is a development of the toroidal type, and consists of two cylindrical resistance coils, mounted side by side, and two wiper arms which make sliding contact with them. Tappings from the coils are arranged and connected so that the device responds in a similar manner to the toroidal transmitter, but is more sensitive to small movements of the wiper arms. The arms are operated by a crank pin, to which the bellows movement is applied; current is conveyed to the arms by two spiral springs.

For each pressure, the bellows locate the wiper arms in a definite position relative to the resistance coils. The output from the transmitter, which depends upon the position of the wiper arms, is conveyed to the indicator which registers the pressure in lb/sq.in.

To prevent mechanical vibration affecting the transmitter mechanism, the unit is supported in a special anti-vibration mounting. The mounting consists of a metal strap suspended on three springs in an outer cradle. The cradle is rigidly secured to the aircraft, and the transmitter is held by the floating strap which grips the transmitter body when a clamping screw, on the strap, is tightened.

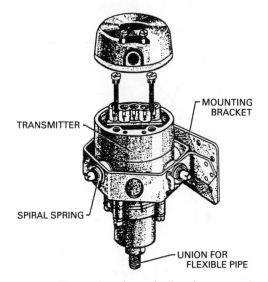

TRANSMITTER

MOUNTING BRACKET

SPIRAL SPRING

UNION FOR FLEXIBLE PIPE

Fig.5-15. Transmitter in anti-vibration mounting.

ELECTRICALLY-OPERATED VALVES

5.18   Introduction

The operating force of these types of valve is obtained by the use of an electro-magnet which consists of a soft iron or steel armature, housed in a non-ferrous metal sleeve, around which a wire is wound to form a coil or solenoid.

Various methods of control of the valve are available. For example, the electric current may be introduced by manual switch if the valve is to be in continuous use, and push-button for intermittent operation. Where automatic control is necessary, a thermostat or pressure switch can be used.

5.19   Pilot Valve

This valve may be included in a hydraulic system to facilitate the selection of a service by remote control. Pressure fluid is admitted at the radial inlet ports and thence to the holes in the valve seat. When the solenoid is energised, the armature is displaced vertically by magnetic attraction, and the valve element, which is pinned to the armature is lifted off its seat. Pressure fluid then escapes past the valve element and out of the valve through the outlet port.

When the solenoid is de-energised, the armature and valve element are returned to their original positions by a spring. The valve element is thus held on its seat, closing the inlet port until the solenoid is again energised.

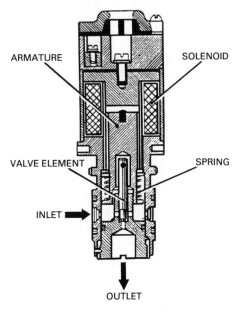

Fig.5-16. Pilot valve.

5.20 Two-way Selector Valve

This valve is used to direct a flow of fluid to a specific service, or alternatively allow fluid from that service to pass to a return line. The electric current to a solenoid operates a pilot valve which directs fluid to control the movement of a slide valve; this in turn directs the main flow of fluid through the selector.

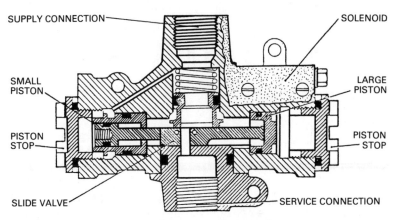

Fig.5-17. Two-way selector valve.

When the solenoid is de-energised, the spindle in the pilot valve is held away from the ball valve by its spring. Fluid from the supply connection then passes along drillings to the pilot valve, forces the ball valve against the return seat, flows past the ball valve and through a drilling to the bore for the large actuating piston. Simultaneously, supply fluid flows from the supply connection direct to the bore for the small actuating piston. The difference in surface area of the pistons causes a greater force to be applied at the large piston and move the slide valve to align its slot with that of the connection block; supply fluid then flows to the service connection.

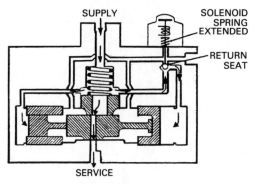

Solenoid De-Energised

When the solenoid is energised, its plunger pushes the spindle of the pilot valve to thrust the ball valve against the pressure seat. The fluid from the supply connection is thus cut off from the bore for the large piston and the pressure on this piston is relieved through the open return seat. Supply fluid flows directly through a drilling to the bore for the small piston, with the result that the slot of the slide valve is moved out of alignment with the slot of the connection block.

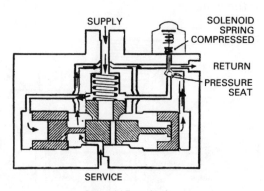

Solenoid Energised

The flow of the supply fluid through the selector is thus cut off and the return fluid at the service connection passes round the end of the slide valve and through a drilling to the return connection.

5.21 Four-way Selector Valve

This valve is used to direct the flow of fluid to one of two services and simultaneously open the return line for the other service. The electric current to either of two solenoids operates a corresponding pilot valve controlling the movement of a slide valve. With both solenoids de-energised, the slide is in neutral or mid-position and there is no flow of fluid through the unit.

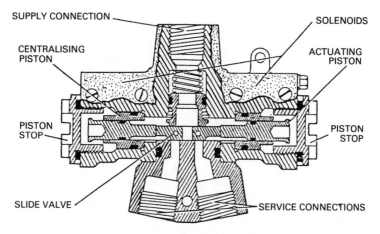

Fig.5-18. Four-way selector valve.

When both solenoids are de-energised, the spindle in each pilot valve is held away from the ball valve by its spring. Fluid from the supply connection then passes along drillings to both pilot valves, forces the ball valves against their return seats, flows past the ball valves and through drillings to the bores of the centralising and actuating pistons.

The fluid pressure, acting equally on both pistons, maintains the slide valve in the central position. Fluid cannot flow through the unit as the slot of the slide valve is midway between the two slots in the connection block.

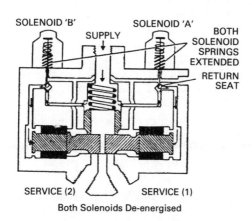

Both Solenoids De-energised

With the energising of one solenoid, for example solenoid B, its plunger pushes the spindle of the pilot valve to thrust the ball valve against the pressure seat. The fluid from the supply connection is thus cut off from the bore of the relevant actuating piston, and the pressure on this piston is relieved through the open return seat. The pressure acting on the opposite actuating piston moves the slide valve along the main bore, and the idle actuating centralising pistons are moved to contact the piston stop; fluid at this end flows to the return connection.

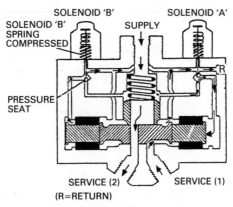

Solenoid 'B' Energised

The slot in the slide valve is now aligned with one of the slots in the connection block and fluid from the supply connection flows to the relevant service connection. With the offset movement of the slide valve, one of the oblique drillings is uncovered and return fluid from the other service connection flows through this drilling to the return connection.

When the solenoid is de-energised, the spring of the pilot valve assembly withdraws the spindle from the ball valve. Fluid in the pressure line forces the ball valve on to the return seat and equal pressure is again applied to the pistons. Whilst the slide valve is offset from the centre, the pressure is applied at one end to the combined areas of the actuating and centralising pistons, both of which are in contact with the slide valve.

The actuating piston only is in contact with the slide valve on the opposite side and therefore the pressure is only effective on this piston area. The differential loading moves the slide valve towards the central position. When the moving centralising piston has reached the limit of its travel, the pressure becomes effective only on the actuating piston and thus becomes equal at each end.

The slide valve, which is then centralised, ceases to move, and in this position the slot in the slide valve is midway between the slots in the connection block. Fluid is therefore trapped in the pipe lines from the service connections until a new selection is made.

Note:
The operation of solenoid A is similar in principle to solenoid B, but the flow of fluid to and from the service connections is reversed.

ACTUATORS

5.22   Introduction

Electrical units that are capable of exerting reversible linear movement, or a reversible turning effort are known as electrical actuators and are used in many aircraft installations where remote control is required, e.g., operation of flaps, trimming tabs, canopy hood, bomb doors, etc. Dependent on their function, actuators are termed either rotary or linear, both of which contain a small electric motor to supply the necessary power. They are self-contained units, and are connected to the equipment to be operated.

5.23   Motor

To obtain reversibility in operation, the majority of actuators are powered by a small split-field series motor, i.e., a motor having two field windings wound in opposite directions. Electrical connections are made from both fields to a switch mechanism, situated in the cockpit, which enables a changeover to be made from one field to the other, thus causing a reversal of rotation of the motor.

The speed of rotation and the amount of rotary movement of the output shaft of the motor depend on its design. For example, the output shaft of a rotary actuator designed for operation of fuel cocks may be required to turn at 3 r.p.m., limited to an angular travel of 90 degrees. The output shaft of a canopy actuator may turn at 50 r.p.m., without any limitation to angular travel, while a cowl gill actuator shaft may turn at 12 r.p.m. and be restricted in angular travel to a pre-determined number of complete revolutions.

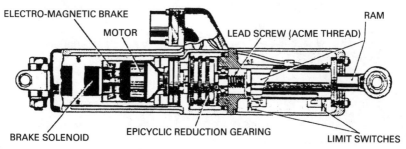

ELECTRO-MAGNETIC BRAKE   RAM

MOTOR   LEAD SCREW (ACME THREAD)

BRAKE SOLENOID   EPICYCLIC REDUCTION GEARING   LIMIT SWITCHES

Fig.5-19. Linear actuator.

5.24   Gearing

The speed of the motor may be over 15,000 r.p.m., and to reduce the speed of the output shaft suitable reduction gearing is used. This gearing may be one or both of two types, epicyclic of multi-stage spur gearing. The gearing reduction ratio of a normal multi-stage spur type can be as low as 21,000:1, and a normal epicyclic type 625:1. Rotary actuators designed for low-speed small-angle operation are usually fitted with multi-stage spur type gears, while linear actuators are fitted with epicyclic gearing or a combination of both gears.

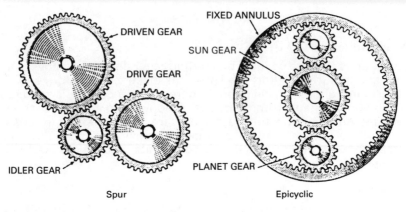

Fig.5-20. Types of reduction gearing.

Annulus Release

In some types of actuator, the first annulus gear may be 'floating' and have an annulus release incorporated. This device, which may be either mechanically or electrically-operated, enables an alternative form of drive to be applied to the load should the electrical supply to the actuator fail. When an alternative drive is not provided, the annulus release may be fitted to allow the component to move to the 'safe' position, e.g., if the electrical supply fails, the airstream would move cowling gills to the fully open position, thus preventing overheating of the engine.

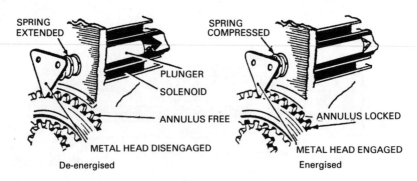

Fig.5-21. Annulus release.

With the electrically-operated type, the first annulus gear is held stationary by the metal head of an electro-magnetic plunger, thus permitting transmission of the drive to the ram. The metal head is three-sided and has two holes for guide pins, which prevent the plunger from being rotated when meshed with the teeth on the outside of the annulus. If the electrical supply to the actuator fails, the electro-magnet is de-energised and the metal head withdrawn by spring pressure, thus the first annulus gear is free and disconnects the drive between motor and ram.

5.25 Lead Screw Threads

In the linear actuator, the motor is coupled through reduction gearing to a lead screw, which extends or retracts a ram or plunger. The thread of the lead screw mates with a corresponding thread in the ram. The lead screw is located and can only turn; it has no freedom in a linear (fore and aft) direction. The ram is prevented from turning, but has freedom of movement in a linear direction, thus the rotary motion of the motor is converted into linear movement of the ram.

Screw-thread of the acme type is usually used in the smaller types of actuator, but a high-efficiency thread that may be termed a 'ball bearing thread' is used in large, powerful actuators. This latter thread consists of two grooves which contain steel balls and replaces the conventional male and female threads; a recirculating device ensures that the steel balls are fed continuously into the grooves as the ram extends or retracts. To prevent rotation of the ram, steel balls are sometimes located in depressions in the outer surface of the ram and travel in slots formed on the inside of the ram housing.

5.26 Limit Switches

To prevent excessive load on the motor at full extent of travel of the output shaft or ram and to control the movement, some form of limit switch is fitted. Limit switches also enable the pilot to make selection without having to worry if full travel will be exceeded. Rotary actuators whose output shafts are designed to rotate not more than one revolution, are usually fitted with internal limit switches; where the movement is greater, external switches, similar to micro switches are operated by the airframe component. In both instances, the switches automatically cut off the electrical supply to the motor when the output shaft or ram has reached its allotted position.

5.27 Electro-magnetic Brake

After the limit switch operates and cuts off the electrical supply, the

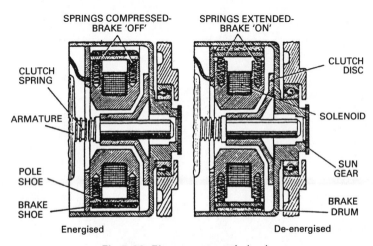

Fig.5-22. Electro-magnetic brake.

motor would tend to continue to rotate due to inertia, but this override or overtravel, is prevented by an electro-magnetic brake. The brake illustrated consists of a brake drum integral with the first sun gear. Screwed to the intermediate housing is an eight-pole brake spider, the solenoid of which is connected in series with the armature of the motor. Across the top of each of the four pairs of pole shoes (only two pairs illustrated) is a cork-lined brake shoe. To maintain pressure between the pole shoes and the inside periphery of the brake drum, small helical springs are fitted.

When the brake solenoid is energised, the pole shoes are attracted, the springs compressed and the brake shoes drawn clear of the brake drum, thereby allowing the motor to rotate the gearing. Immediately the electrical supply is switched off, either by operation of the control switch, or by the limit switches, the brake solenoid is de-energised and the brake shoes released. The springs then extend and force the brake shoes against the brake drum, thus preventing override.

5.28 Clutch

To prevent damage to the motor, which can be caused by excessive load on the output shaft, the drive from the motor to the reduction gearing may pass through a spring-loaded clutch. This allows the motor to slip, should excessive overloading of the output shaft occur.

5.29 Indicator

Indication of the position of the actuated equipment or component may be shown on the actuator by wording, e.g., OPEN and SHUT, or there may be additional contact surfaces incorporated in the actuator limit switches, which are connected by electrical wiring to a panel-mounted indicator in the cockpit.

CHAPTER 5
TEST YOURSELF QUESTIONS
COMPONENTS

1. A fuse may be replaced by the pilot:
    (a) only after consulting an engineer.
    (b) once, then the engineer must be consulted.
    (c) never, it must always be replaced by an engineer.
    (d) twice, and then the engineer must be consulted.

    Ref. Ch.5. Para.5.4.

2. A Rheostat is:
    (a) a temperature control device.
    (b) a remote automatic manual switch.
    (c) a variable resistor.
    (d) a temperature indicator.

    Ref. Ch.5. Para.5.5.

3. A Relay:
    (a) is a form of mechanical switch.
    (b) is a form of electro magnetic switch.
    (c) is a form of connecter.
    (d) is a form of temperature sensing device.

    Ref. Ch.5. Para.5.6.

4. Bonding:
    (a) ensures electro static potential difference is maintained.
    (b) ensures electro static potential difference is minimised.
    (c) is used to reduce radio interference.
    (d) is used to earth negative connecters.

    Ref. Ch.5. Para.5.8.

5. In the event generator voltage falls below battery voltage:
    (a) reverse current to the generator is prevented by the cut-out.
    (b) the generator will remain connected to the bus-bar.
    (c) the battery will automatically be disconnected from the bus-bar.
    (d) the cut-out will disconnect the battery from the system.

    Ref. Ch.5. Para.5.12.

6. A micro switch is an assembly:
   (a) of very small dimensions.
   (b) has a very small movement to make or break a circuit.
   (c) is used for instrument contact only.
   (d) is used where one side of the structure is inaccessible.
   Ref. Ch.5. Para.5.16.

7. The limit switches of a linear actuator:
   (a) limit the travel of the actuator.
   (b) prevent excessive loads on the actuator.
   (c) illuminate the actuator lights when the actuator is on.
   (d) prevent overtravel of the actuator.
   Ref. Ch.5. Para.5.26.

8. Ground power:
   (a) output must be the same as aircraft output before it is connected.
   (b) output must be paralleled with aircraft output before it is connected.
   (c) output must be on minimum before it is connected.
   (d) must be 'off' before it is connected to the aircraft.
   Ref. Ch.5 Para.5.14.

9. Generator voltage:
   (a) is controlled by the cut-out.
   (b) is controlled by the voltage regulator.
   (c) is controlled by the number of magnetic poles.
   (d) is controlled by the R.P.M. of the engine.
   Ref. Ch.5 Para.5.11.

10. When a ground/flight switch is set to:
   (a) 'ground', power is supplied for ground operations.
   (b) 'ground', power is off.
   (c) 'flight', power is off.
   (d) 'ground', the electrical circuits are earthed to ground.
   Ref. Ch.5 Para.5.14.

6

THE GENERATION OF ALTERNATING CURRENT

6.1 Introduction

Modern aircraft utilize electrical power to operate an ever increasing number of aircraft systems and sub-systems, and the power requirements for a modern airliner are such that considerable advantage may be gained from the use of alternating generators, otherwise known as alternators. The saving of weight and space in modern aircraft is of the utmost importance, and in the electrical sense, with the use of alternating current (A.C.) devices, considerable saving can be made of both. In particular, the use of A.C. Generators and Motors, are particularly advantageous as they are generally smaller and simpler than their D.C. equivalents. In the past brush wear, i.e., wear of the pick up points, has been a serious problem through arcing at altitude, this, however, in modern A.C. Generators has been eliminated.

Another advantage is that most aircraft using 24 volt D.C. supply, have a requirement for a certain amount of 400 cycle A.C. Supply voltages from A.C. sources can also be converted from higher to lower voltages or vice versa, with almost 100 per cent efficiency which is a major advantage.

6.2 Comparison of A.C and D.C.

Some of the principles, characteristics and effects of A.C. are similar to those of D.C. Equally so, there are a number of differences; these are explained later. Direct current flows in one direction only, and has constant polarity. The only change of magnitude occurs when the circuit is switched on or off; See Figure 6-1, D.C. Wave Form.

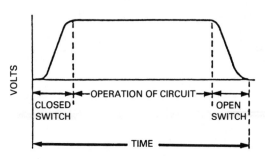

Fig.6-1. D.C. Wave form.

Alternating current on the other hand, changes direction and therefore polarity at regular intervals. It increases in value at the definite rate; decreases to zero having completed a half cycle, then repeats the process but in a negative sense in the other direction. This is referred to as a full 360 degrees cycle and is sinusoidal in form, there is therefore a current flow in one direction for half the cycle, and a flow in the opposite direction for the second half of the cycle. See Figure 6-2.

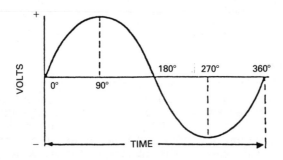

Fig.6-2. A.C. Wave form.

6.3 Origin of Sine Wave

In Figure 6-3 the origin of the sine wave is shown in diagrammatic form. If OP rotates in the direction shown at a constant angular velocity w, the length of ON will vary according to OP sin wt where t equals time of rotation. OP is regarded as a vector of the same magnitude as Yo, the projection therefore of OP on Oy, will show instantaneous value of a quantity which is alternating sinusoidally, and the peak value will be Yo.

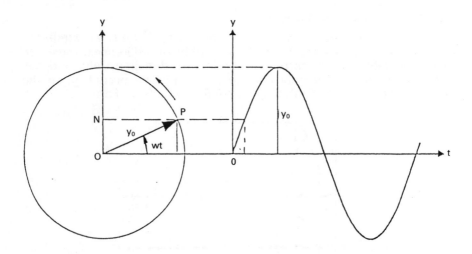

Fig.6-3. Origin of Sine Wave.

6.4 Principles of Generating Electricity

Following the discovery that an electric current flowing through a conductor creates a magnetic field around the conductor, the English scientist Faraday showed that the reverse was also true, that is, if a conductor was passed through a magnetic field then a voltage would be induced in the conductor and current would flow.

Figures 6-4a, b and c demonstrate the above principles.

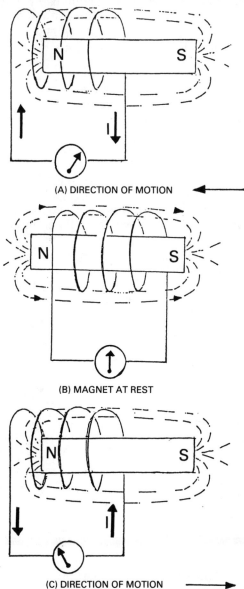

(A) DIRECTION OF MOTION ◄───────

(B) MAGNET AT REST

(C) DIRECTION OF MOTION ───────►

Fig.6-4. Principle of Current Generation.

Figure 6-4a shows a bar magnet being moved through a coil of wire i.e. a conductor, in the direction shown by the arrow. As the lines of force of the magnetic field move through the coil, an electromotive force or voltage is induced in it, and a current will flow in the circuit in the direction shown, and will be measured by the galvonometer.

When the magnet is withdrawn from the coil, a voltage will again be induced, and a current will flow but in the opposite direction. Therefore it can be seen there will only be a voltage induced when there is relative motion between the magnetic field and the conductor.

Note must always be made, with reference to Figure 6-5a and 6-5b, the maximum e.m.f. induced will be when the conductor cuts the lines of magnetic force of the magnetic field at right angles. Figure 6-5a shows maximum e.m.f. being induced; Figure 6-5b shows the conductor moving parallel to the lines of magnetic force and so no e.m.f. will be induced, therefore no current will flow.

As the lines of force of the magnetic field move through the coil, an electromotive force or voltage is induced in it, and a current will flow in the circuit in the direction shown, and will be measured by the galvonometer.

When the magnet is withdrawn from the coil, a voltage will again be induced, and a current will flow but in the opposite direction as shown in Figure 4. Only therefore, when there is relative motion between the magnetic field and the conductor will there be an induced voltage.

Further to the above, and with reference to Figures 5a and 5b, the maximum e.m.f. induced will be when the conductor cuts the lines of force of the magnetic field at right angles. Figure 5a shows maximum e.m.f. being induced; Figure 5b shows the conductor moving parallel to the magnetic field, and in this case no e.m.f. will be induced, therefore no current will flow.

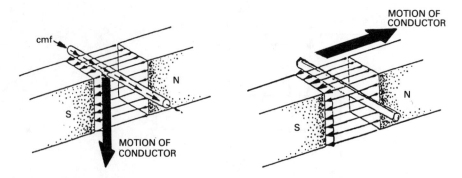

Fig.6-5a. E.M.F. being induced.   *Fig.6-5b. No E.M.F. induced.*

6.5   The Basic Principles of the A.C. Generator

In its simplest form an A.C. Generator, or Alternator consists of a coil rotating in a uniform magnetic field. See Figure 6-6.

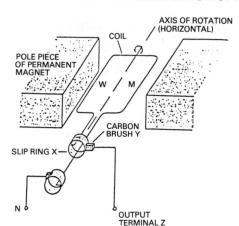

Fig.6-6. Principle of an A.C. Generator.

The generator current which is induced in the rotating coil is fed from the coil in such a way that each side of the coil is always connected to the same terminal output, no matter what the orientation of the coil. This is achieved by the use of slip rings. Side W of the coil is attached to slip ring X. This rubs against brush Y which is connected to output terminal Z. Thus, W is always in electrical contact with Z. Similarly, side M of the coil is always in electrical contact with output terminal N, and therefore the alternating e.m.f. of the rotating coil appears at the output terminals. See Figure 6-6.

As with the D.C. Generator the magnetic field of the A.C. Generator is provided by an electromagnetic. The coils of the electromagnet are called field coils, or field windings, and are wound onto soft iron poles. In the same way as the D.C. Generator, the field windings are energised by current supplied as D.C. and is normally controlled by a voltage regulator.

Figure 6-7 shows the basic operation so far.

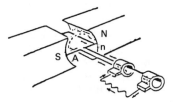

Fig.6-7a. Inducing maximum voltage in an elementary generator.

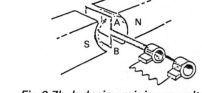

Fig.6-7b. Inducing minimum voltage in an elementary generator.

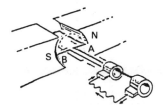

Fig.6-7c. Inducing maximum voltage in the opposite direction.

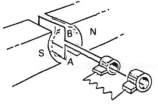

Fig.6-7d. Inducing a minimum voltage in the opposite direction.

Figure 6-7 shows a loop of wire, conductor, rotating in a magnetic field in a clockwise direction.

In Figures 6-7a and 6-7b the position of the loop shows maximum and minimum induced voltages for the positive half cycle, whilst Figures 6-7c and 6-7d show the maximum and minimum voltage induction for the negative half.

This can now be related to Figure 6-8 which shows the complete wave form of alternating current which has been generated.

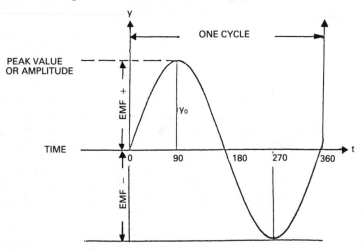

Fig.6-8. Output of an elementary generator.

6.6 Basic Construction and Operation

In the principles so far given in this chapter, the magnetic poles have been shown as stationary and the armature loop the rotating member. In reality modern A.C. Generators normally have the armature fixed, or stationary, and the magnetic poles the rotating member. The primary reason for this is the rotating slip rings need only be capable of handling the smaller of the two currents. In such an arrangement the armature becomes known as the stator and the magnetic poles the rotor. Figure 6-9 shows a comparison of the two arrangements, that is the rotating armature as used on most D.C. Generators and the fixed armature, or stator, as used on most A.C. Types.

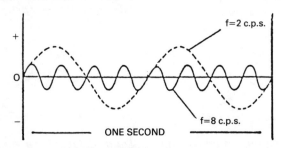

Fig.6-9. Cycle and frequency.

6.7 Generator or Alternator Frequency

Frequency can be defined as the number of cycles of an A.C. wave form generated per second, and the unit of frequency is the 'Hertz' (Hz). One Hertz is equal to one cycle per second.

The frequency of an alternator depends upon;

(a) the number of pairs of magnetic poles, and

(b) the speed of rotation of the rotor.

This may be found from: $\text{c.p.s.} = \dfrac{\text{r.p.m.} \times \text{no of pairs of poles}}{60}$

For example, a six pole generator with a rotational speed of 8000 r.p.m. would give:

$\dfrac{8000 \times 3}{60} = 400$ c.p.s. or 400 Hz.

For aircraft constant frequency systems, 400Hz has been adopted as the standard. There are essentially two types of A.C. Generator used on aircraft with regard to frequency, the constant frequency, or constant speed type, as mentioned above, which is controlled to produce a frequency of 400Hz. The other type is uncontrolled, that is to say, Frequency Wild, and may produce a frequency between approximately 100Hz and 1200Hz. These types will be discussed in detail later.

6.8 Inductance

When alternating current flows through a coil of wire, the rise and fall of the current flow, first in one direction, and then in another, sets up an expanding and collapsing magnetic field about the coil. A voltage is induced in the coil which is opposite in direction to the applied voltage and which opposes any change in the alternating current. The induced voltage is called the counter electro motive force (c.e.m.f.), since it opposes the applied voltage.

This property of a coil to oppose any change in the current flowing through it is called inductance.

The inductance of a coil is measured in Henrys. In any coil, the inductance depends on several factors, principally the number of turns, the cross sectional area of the coil, and the material in the centre of the coil, or core. A core of magnetic material greatly increases the inductance of the coil.

It must be remembered, however, that even a straight wire has inductance, small though it may be when compared with that of a coil. A.C. Motors, relays, and transformers contribute inductance to a circuit. Practically all A.C. circuits contain inductive elements.

The symbol for inductance in formulas is the capital letter 'L'. Inductance is measured in henrys (abbreviated h). An inductor (coil) has an inductance of 1 henry if an e.m.f. of 1 volt is induced in the inductor when the current through the inductor is changing at the rate of 1 ampere per second. However, the henry is a large unit of inductance and is used with relatively large inductors usually having iron cores. The unit normally used for small air core inductors is the millihenry (mh). For still smaller air core inductors the unit of inductance is the microhenry (μh).

If all other circuit values remain constant, the greater the inductance in a coil, the greater the effect of self induction, or opposition to the change in the value of current. As the frequency increases, the inductive reactance increases, since the greater the rate of current change the more the opposition to change by the coil increases. Therefore, inductive reactance is proportional to inductance and frequency.

Inductors may be connected in a circuit in the same manner as resistors. When connected in series, the total inductance is the sum of the inductances in the inductors. When two or more inductors are connected in parallel, the total inductance is, like resistances in parallel, less than that of the smallest inductor.

Figure 6-10 shows an example of an inductor in a circuit.

6.9 Inductance Reactance

The opposition to the flow of current which inductances put in a circuit is called inductance reactance. The symbol for inductive resistance, or reactance, is X_L, and is measured in ohms, just as resistance is.

So $X_L = 2\pi fL$

where X_L = inductance reactance in ohms

f = frequency in cycles per second.

π = 3.1416.

In any circuit in which there is only resistance, the expression for the relationship of voltage and current is Ohms Law.

$$\text{Current} = \frac{\text{Voltage}}{\text{Reactance}} \quad \text{or} \quad I \frac{E}{X_L}$$

where X_L = inductive reactance of the circuit in ohms.

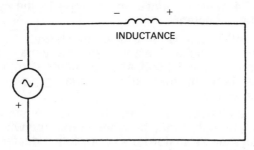

Fig.6-10. A.C. Circuit containing inductance.

6.10 Capacitance

Another important property in an A.C. circuit, besides resistance and inductance, is capacitance. While inductance is represented in a circuit by a coil, capacitance is represented by a capacitor.

Any two conductors separated by a nonconductor, called a dielectric, constitute a capacitor. In an electrical circuit a capacitor serves as a reservoir, or storehouse, for electricity.

Figure 6-11 shows a capacitor in a D.C. circuit and Figure 6-12 a capacitor in an A.C. circuit.

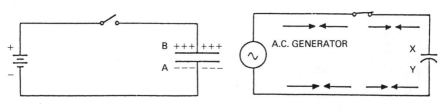

Fig.6-11. Capacitor in a D.C. circuit.   *Fig.6-12. Capacitor in an A.C. circuit.*

When a capacitor is connected across a source of direct current such as a storage battery, such as that shown in Figure 6-11 and the switch is then closed, the plate marked B becomes positively charged, and the plate marked A negatively charged. Current flows in the external circuit during the time the electrons are moving from plate B to A. The current flow in the circuit is maximum the instant the switch is closed, but continually decreases thereafter until it reaches zero. The current becomes zero as soon as the difference in voltage of A and B plates becomes the same as the voltage of the battery. If the switch is opened, the plates remain charged. However, the capacitor quickly discharges if it is short circuited.

The amount of electricity a capacitor can store depends on several factors, including the type of material of the dielectric. It is directly proportional to the plate area and inversely proportional to the distance between the plates.

If a source of alternating current is substituted for the battery, the capacitor acts quite differently than it does with direct current. When alternating current is impressed on the circuit as shown in Figure 6-12, the charge on the plates constantly changes. This means that electricity must flow first from Y clockwise around to X, then from X counterclockwise around to Y, then from Y clockwise around to X, and so on. Although no current flows through the insulator between the plates of the capacitor, it constantly flows in the remainder of the circuit between X and Y. In a circuit in which there is only capacitance, current leads the impressed voltage as contrasted with a circuit in which there is inductance, where the current lags the voltage.

The unit of measurement of capacitance is the Farad, for which the symbol is the letter 'f'. The Farad is too large for practical use and the units generally used are the microfarad (μf), one millionth of a Farad, and the micromicrofarad ($\mu\mu$f), one millionth of a microfarad.

6.11 Capacitance Reactance

Capacitance, like inductance, offers opposition to the flow of current.

This opposition is called capacitive reactance and is measured in ohms. The symbol for capacitive reactance is X.

The Equation:

Current   Voltage   or
         Capacititive Reactance

$$I = \frac{E}{X_c}$$

Is similar to Ohms Law and the equation for current in an inductive circuit. The greater the frequency in a capacitive circuit, the less the reactance. Hence, the capacitive reactance:

$$X = \frac{I}{2\eta \times f \times C}$$

Where f = frequency in c.p.s.
      C = capacity in Farads.
      2η = 6.28.

6.12 The Phase Relationship of Current and Voltage in the Generation of Alternating Current

Figures 6-13a and 6-13b, show what is referred to as the phase relationship of voltage and current in a sinusoidal wave form.

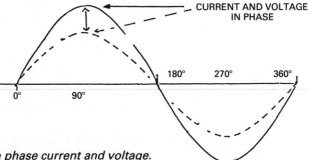

Fig.6-13a. In phase current and voltage.

Figure 6-13a shows the voltage and current to be 'in phase', that is to say, the values of both are maximum and minimum at the same time. In a circuit with a purely resistive load, the voltage and current are in phase.

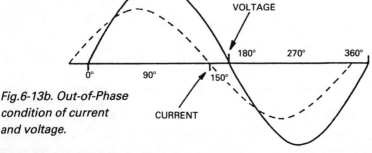

Fig.6-13b. Out-of-Phase condition of current and voltage.

Figure 6-13b shows the current lagging the voltage by 30 degrees; they are said to be out of phase. In a circuit with an inductive load, the current lags the voltage by 90 degrees.

Phase Relationships in A.C. Circuits with Resistive, Inductive and Capacitive Loads

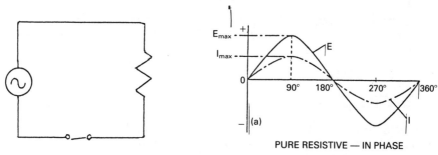

PURE RESISTIVE — IN PHASE

Fig.6-14a. In a circuit with a purely resistive load, the voltage and current are in phase.

In a circuit with a capacitive load the current leads the voltage by 90 degrees.

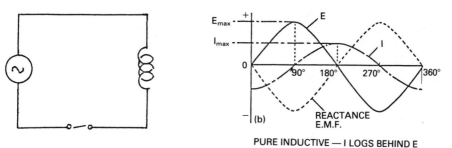

PURE INDUCTIVE — I LOGS BEHIND E

Fig.6-14b. In circuit with an inductive load, the current lags the voltage by 90 degrees.

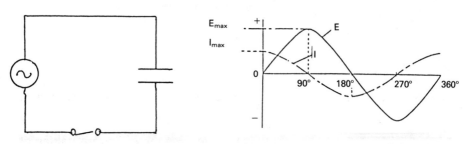

Figure 6-14 shows current leading voltage in a capacitive circuit.

Fig.6-14c. In a circuit with capacitive load, the current leads the voltage by 90 degrees.

6.13 Root Mean Square Values

If an alternating current flowing in a circuit produces the same heating effect as a direct current of (say) 3A flowing in the same circuit, then the effective value of the alternating current is also 3A. In general, the effective value of the alternating current is equal to that direct current which results in the same expenditure of energy under the same conditions.

The energy, W, supplied in time, t, by an alternating current, I, flowing through a restistance, R, is given by the product of t and the average value of I^2R, i.e.

$$W = (I^2R)_{avge}\ t$$

since R is constant, this becomes

$$W = (I^2)_{avge}\ Rt$$

If (anticipating the result) the effective value of I is denoted by I_{RMS}, then W is equal to the energy supplied by a steady current of magnitude I_{RMS} flowing through a resistance R for time t, i.e.

$$W = (I_{RMS})^2\ Rt$$

Therefore, from the above equations,

$$(I_{RMS})^2\ Rt = (I^2)_{avge}\ Rt$$

i.e. $I_{RMS} \quad = \sqrt{(I^2)_{avge}}$

i.e. $I_{RMS} \quad = \sqrt{\text{average value of } I^2}$

Thus, the effective value (denoted by I_{RMS}) is the root mean square (RMS) value and the reason for the notation is now clear. This equation holds for any alternating current but the relationship between I_{RMS} and the peak value, I_o, depends on the nature of the A.C.

Sinusoidal A.C.

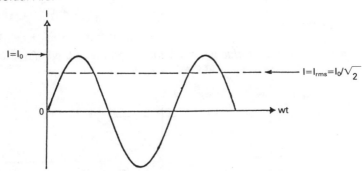

Fig.6-15. To illustrate the relationship between a sinusoidal alternating current and its RMS value.

From the above it can be shown that the root mean square values of A.C. current and voltage are:

$$I_{rms} = I_o/\sqrt{2}\ = 0.7071_o \text{ and}$$
$$E_{rms} = E_o/\sqrt{2} = 0.707E_o$$

6.14 Power Ratings of A.C. Generators

The power ratings of alternating current generators are usually given in kilovolt-amps (kVA) rather than kilowatts (kW) as in the case of D.C. generators.

The main reason for this is due to the fact that in calculating the power, account must be taken of the difference between the true or effective power, and the apparent power.

This difference arises from the type of circuit which the generator is to supply, and the phase relationships of voltage and current. This is expressed as a ratio termed the power factor (P.F.) and may be written as:

$$\text{P.F.} = \frac{\text{Effective power (kW)}}{\text{Apparent power (kVA)}} = \cos \text{ phase angle}$$

If the voltage and current are in phase as in a resistive circuit, the power factor is 100% or 'unity'; the reason being that the effective power and apparent power are equal, therefore a generator rated at 100 kVA in a circuit with a power factor of unity, will have an output which is 100% efficient and exactly equal to 100 kW.

When a circuit contains inductance or capacitance however, current and voltage will not be in phase; this will then make the P.F. less than unity.

Figure 6-16 shows a vector diagram for a current I lagging a voltage E, by an angle ϕ.

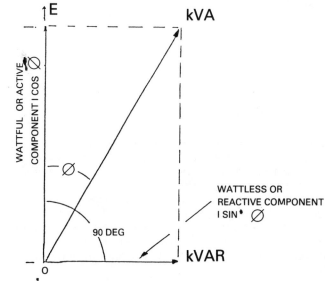

Fig.6-16. Current/Voltage.

The current is resolved into two components at right angles to each other, one is in phase with E, and is given by I cos ϕ, and the other out of phase by 90 degrees or 'in quadrature', given by I sin ϕ. The in phase component is called the active 'wattful' or working component (kW), and the other is referred to as the idle, wattless or reactive component (kVAR).

The importance of these two components will become more apparent when later, methods of load sharing between generators are discussed.

Most A.C. generators are designed to take a proportion of the reactive component of current through their windings. Some indication of this may be obtained from the information given on the generator data plate. As an example, the output rating may be specified as 40 kVA at .8 P.F. This would mean that the maximum output in kW is .8 × 40 or 32 kW, but that the product of volts and amperes under all conditions of P.F. must not exceed 40 kVA.

6.15   Further Illustrations of Power in A.C. Circuits

In a D.C. circuit, power is obtained by the equation, P = EI, (watts equal volts times amperes). Thus if 1 ampere of current flows in a circuit at a pressure of 200 volts, the power is 200 watts. The product of the volts and the amperes is the true power in the circuit.

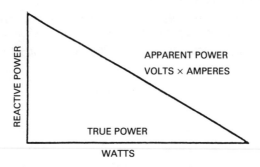

Fig.6-17. Power relations in A.C. circuit.

In an A.C. circuit, a voltmeter indicates the effective voltage and an ammeter indicates the effective current. The product of these two readings is called the apparent power. Only when the A.C. circuit is made up of pure resistance is the apparent power equal to the true power Figure 6.17. When there is a capacitance or inductance in the circuit, the current and voltage are not exactly in phase, and the true power is less than the apparent power. The true power is obtained by a wattmeter reading. The ratio of the true power to the apparent power is called the power factor and is usually expressed in percent. In equation form, the relationship is:

$$\text{Power Factor (PF)} = \frac{100 \times \text{Watts (True Power)}}{\text{Volts} \times \text{Amperes (Apparent Power)}}$$

Problem:
A 220 volt A.C. motor takes 50 amperes from the line, but a wattmeter in the line shows that only 9,350 watts are taken by the motor. What is the apparent power and the power factor?

Solution:

Apparent power = Volts × Amperes

Apparent power = 220 × 50 = 11,000 watts or volt-amperes.

$$PF = \frac{Watts\ (True\ Power) \times 100}{VA\ (Apparent\ Power)}$$

$$PF = \frac{9,350 \times 100}{11,000} = 85\ or\ 85\%$$

6.16 Rectification of A.C.

Rectification is the process of changing alternating current to direct current. When a semi-conductor rectifier, such as a junction diode, is connected to an A.C. voltage source, it is alternately biased forward and reverse, in step with the A.C. voltage, as shown in Figure 6-18.

In Figure 6-19, a diode is placed in series with a source of A.C power and a load resistor. This is called a half-wave rectifier circuit.

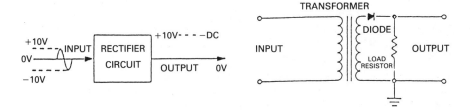

Fig.6-18. Rectification process.   *Fig.6-19. Half-wave rectifier circuit.*

The transformer provides the A.C. input to the circuit; the diode provides the rectification of the A.C.; and the load resistor serves two purposes: (1) It limits the amount of current flow in the circuit to a safe level, and (2) it develops an output signal due to the current flow through it.

Assume, in Figure 6-20 that the top of the transformer secondary is positive and the bottom negative. With this polarity, the diode is forward-biased, resistance of the diode is very low, and current flows through the circuit in the direction of the arrows. The output (voltage drop) across the load resistor follows the waveshape of the positive half of the A.C. input. When the A.C. input goes in a negative direction, the top of the transformer secondary becomes negative and the diode becomes reverse-biased.

With reverse bias applied to the diode, the resistance of the diode becomes very great, and current flow through the diode and load resistor becomes zero. (Remember that a very small current will flow through the diode). The output, taken across the load resistor, will be zero. If the position of the diode was reversed, the output would be negative pulses.

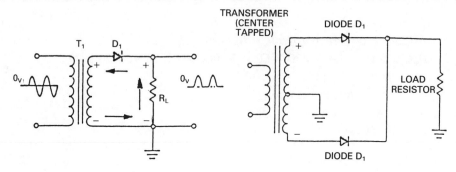

Fig.6-20. Output of a half-wave
rectifier.

Fig.6-21. Full-wave rectifier.

In a half-wave rectifier, a half cycle of power is produced across the load resistor for each full cycle of input power. To increase the output power, a full-wave rectifier can be used. Figure 6-21 shows a full-wave rectifier, which is, in effect, two half-wave rectifiers combined into one circuit. In this circuit a load resistor is used to limit current flow and develop an output voltage, two diodes to provide rectification, and a transformer to provide an A.C. input to the circuit. The transformer, used in full-wave rectifier circuits, must be centre tapped to complete the path for current flow through the load resistor.

Assuming the polarities shown on the transformer, diode D_1 will be forward-biased and current will flow from ground through the load resistor, through diode D_1 to the top of the transformer.

When the A.C. input changes direction, the transformer secondary will assume an opposite polarity.

6.17 Diode Bridge Rectifier Circuit

An advantageous modification to the full-wave diode rectifier is the bridge rectifier, see Figure 6-22a, b, c. The bridge rectifier differs from the full-wave rectifier in that a bridge rectifier does not require a centre-tapped transformer, but does require two additional diodes.

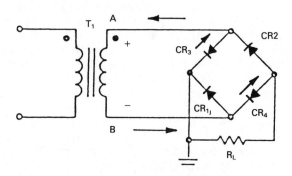

Fig.6-22a. Diode bridge rectifier.

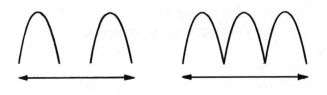

Fig.6-22b.   Fig.6-22c.

Half-wave and full-wave rectifier outputs

Elements used in rectifiers include: the *Semi-conductor* type, the *Silicon rectifier*, and the *Selenium* rectifier.

CHAPTER 6
TEST YOURSELF QUESTIONS

1. In an A.C. Generator:
   (a) the moving member is termed the armature.
   (b) the moving member is termed the inductance coil.
   (c) the moving member is termed the rotational coil.
   (d) the moving member is termed the rotor.

   Ref. Ch.6. Para.6.6.

2. In a circuit with purely resistive loads:
   (a) voltage leads current.
   (b) current lags voltage.
   (c) voltage and current are in phase.
   (d) voltage lags current.

   Ref. Ch.6. Para.6.12.

3. In an inductive circuit:
   (a) voltage leads current.
   (b) voltage and current are in phase.
   (c) voltage lags current.
   (d) current leads voltage.

   Ref. Ch.6. Para.6.12.

4. In a capacitive circuit:
   (a) voltage and current are in phase.
   (b) voltage leads current.
   (c) voltage lags current.
   (d) voltage and capacitance are in phase.

   Ref. Ch.6. Para.6.12.

5. In an A.C. Supply system, A.C. is converted to D.C. by:
   (a) a commutator.
   (b) an inverter.
   (c) a rectifier.
   (d) a transformer.

   Ref. Ch.6. Para.6.16.

7

A.C. GENERATORS

7.1 Introduction

The following is a general description of the basic types of generator, or alternator, currently used on aircraft.

Alternating current generators are generally of two main types; those designed for operation over a wide variable speed and variable frequency range (frequency-wild generators), and those designed for constant speed and constant frequency operation (constant-speed generators).

7.2 Frequency-wild Generators

There are basically two categories; those used on small aircraft to provide a direct current voltage output, after rectification, and those used to provide an alternating current voltage output to supply systems that do not require a fixed frequency supply.

Figure 7-1 shows a generator, the output of which is rectified to provide direct current. Generators of this type are utilised in a variety of small aircraft requiring direct current as the primary power source. The main components of the generator are the rotor, the stator, and a rectifier assembly. The rotor consists of two extruded steel pole pieces pressed on to a shaft against each end of a field coil. Each pole piece has six 'fingers', so shaped that when the pole pieces are in position, the 'fingers' mesh with, but do not touch, each other. Two slip rings are pressed onto one end of the rotor shaft and are electrically connected to the rotor field coil. The rotor is rotated by a driving belt and pulley driven by the engine, or by coupling the generator directly to the engine gearbox drive shaft. The stator comprises three star-connected coils wound around a laminated core; each end of each coil is connected to the rectifier assembly while the other ends are joined together to form the 'star' or neutral point. The rectifier assembly is located opposite to the drive-end of the generator, and consists of six silicon diodes connected to form a full-wave bridge rectifier circuit.

Three of the diodes (negative) are mounted on the end frame, while the other three (positive diodes) are mounted on a 'heat sink' plate on the inside of the end frame. Spring-loaded brushes are located inside the end frame and make contact with the rotor slip rings to complete the field or excitation coil circuit.

These small generators do not usually incorporate permanent magnets and are not self excited. They therefore require a supply of direct current from an independent source for the initial excitation of the rotor field windings. In the type illustrated in Figure 1, this is provided from

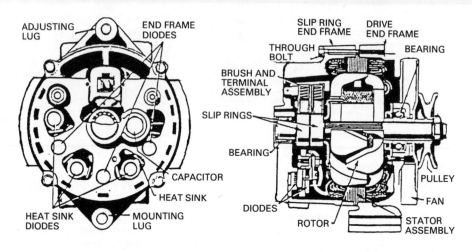

Fig.7-1. Example small brushless D.C. generator.

the busbar of the electrical system of the aircraft when the battery, or an external power supply, is connected to that busbar. The current passing through the field coil circuit causes the 'fingers' of the rotor pole pieces to become alternately north and south electro-magnetic poles. As it rotates, the magnetic field set up in the rotor poles induces a three-phase alternating voltage in the stator windings at a frequency dependent on rotor speed. The output is supplied to the rectifier assembly, and the direct current thus obtained is then supplied to the electrical system busbar, thereby maintaining excitation of the field coil. The rectified output is also fed to a voltage regulator which is pre-set to regulate the generator voltage, within the limits specified for the generator and aircraft electrical system.

Figure 7-2 shows a typical three-phase, frequency-wild generator, which is used in some aircraft for the supply of alternating current to electrical systems that do not require a fixed frequency supply, such as resistive load circuits for de-icing and anti-icing systems. This generator has a power output of 15 kVA at 208 volts, and its frequency and driven speed ranges are 335 to 535 Hz and 6700 to 10700 rpm, respectively. The generator consists of two major assemblies; a rotor assembly and a fixed stator assembly. The rotor assembly has six poles, each of which is wound with a field coil; the coils terminate at two slip rings secured at one end of the rotor shaft. Three spring-loaded brushes are equi-spaced on each slip ring, and are contained within a brushgear housing. The brushes are electrically connected to direct current input terminals housed in an excitation terminal box mounted on the outside of the brushgear housing. The terminal box also houses capacitors connected between the terminals and earth, to suppress interference which may affect, for example, the reception of radio signals. The rotor shaft is splined at the drive end, and supported in a roller bearing fitted in the main housing. An oil seal is provided to prevent the entry of oil from the driving source into the main housing. The stator windings are star-connected, and an end frame clamps the whole assembly in the main housing, which has an integral flange for mounting the generator at the corresponding drive shaft outlet of the engine accessory gearbox. The ends of the stator windings are brought out to a three-way output terminal box mounted on the end frame. The generator is cooled by ram air passing into the main housing via an inlet spout; the air escapes from the main housing through ventilation slots at the drive end, from where it is usually ducted overboard.

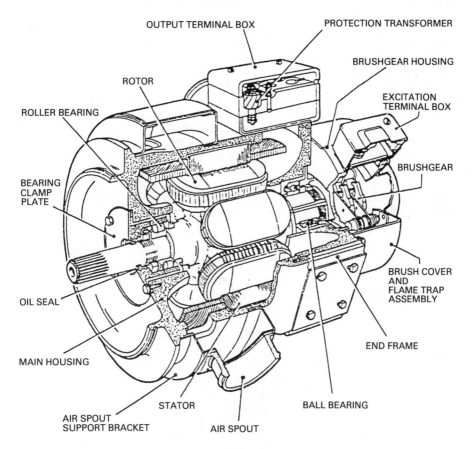

Fig.7-2. Example larger frequency-wild generator.

Direct current for the initial excitation of the rotor field windings is provided from the main busbar via a 'start' switch in the circuit to the excitation terminals and brushgear. As the generator rotates, a three-phase alternating voltage is induced in the stator windings which is supplied to the busbar distribution. The output voltage is controlled by feeding it to a voltage regulator, and to a three-phase bridge rectifier, which together with other protection circuits, are contained within a separate control unit. At a pre-determined output voltage, the generator is able to run as a self-excited machine, and could operate independently of the direct current supply from the main busbar.

7.3   Constant-Speed/Frequency Generators

These generators are utilised in those types of aircraft requiring (i) a much wider application of alternating current, (ii) a considerable amount of electrical power and (iii) generator system load-sharing capability. Generators designed for such applications are currently of the brushless type, and are driven by an engine through the medium of a special constant-speed drive unit. In most applications, the generators may be removed and installed separately and with the drive unit 'in-situ', but for certain types of aircraft, the generators are integrated with the drive unit so that removal and installation as a complete assembly is necessary. Examples of both types are shown in Figures 7.3 and 7.4 respectively. The constant-speed drive is basically a differential gear transmission system which converts variable input speed of an engine to a constant output speed appropriate to the generator rating. The output speed of the generator is controlled by a hydromechanical governor system. The construction of generators varies, but, in general, they consist of three principal components; a pilot exciter, a main exciter and rotating rectifier, and a main generator. All three components are contained within a casing made up of an end bell section and a stator housing section. A mounting flange, which is an integral part of the stator housing section, provides for attachment of the generator to the constant-speed drive unit by means of either studs and retaining nuts, or a quick attach/detach coupling.

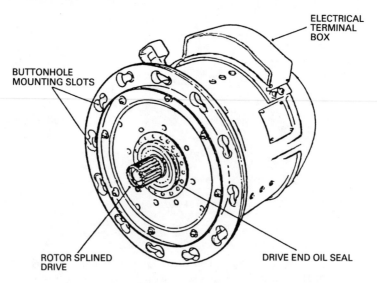

Fig.7-3. Typical constant-speed generator.

The purpose of the pilot exciter is to provide the magnetic field necessary for initial excitation of the main exciter. It comprises a stator, and a permanent magnet rotor which is mounted on the same shaft as the main exciter and main generator rotor. The A.C. output from the pilot exciter is fed to the main exciter field via a control and protection unit.

The rotating rectifier assembly supplies excitation current to the main generator rotor field coils from the main exciter rotor, and eliminates the need for brushes and slip rings. It usually consists of six silicon diodes connected as a three-phase, full-wave bridge rectifier circuit, sometimes contained within a tubular insulator located in the hollow shaft on which both the exciter rotor and main generator rotor are mounted, but can be mounted in any convenient position on the rotor, provided the radius from the centre line is not excessive.

The main generator consists of a three-phase, star-wound stator, a rotor and associated field windings, which are connected to the rotating rectifier assembly. The leads from the three stator phases are connected to a terminal block, which permits connection of the generator to the aircraft power distribution system.

When a generator starts operating, an initial flow of current is provided to the field of the main exciter via the control and protection unit, and a three-phase voltage is produced in the exciter rotor. This voltage is then supplied to the rotating rectifier assembly, the direct current output of which is, in turn, fed to the field coils of the main generator as the required excitation current. A rotating magnetic field is thus produced which induces a three-phase voltage output of 200 volts, at a frequency of 400 Hz, in the main stator windings. The output voltage is sensed at the busbar by the voltage regulator, which controls the amount of excitation current required by the main generator section to maintain the desired A.C. output.

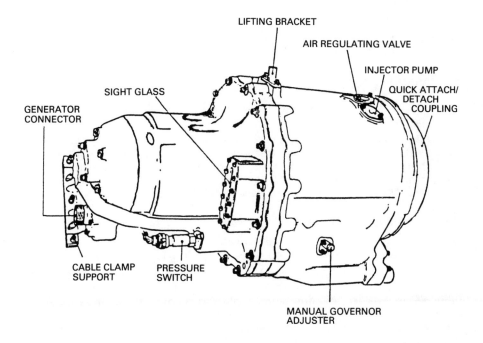

Fig.7-4. Example integrated drive generator.

Generator cooling is normally provided by ram air which enters through the end bell section of the casing, and passes through the windings, the rotor shaft, and the rectifier assembly. The air is exhausted through a perforated screen around the periphery of the casing, at a point adjacent to the main generator stator, then usually ducted overboard. In the case of integrated drive generators, cooling of the windings and rectifier assembly is provided by oil which is also used for the speed governing hydraulic system. The oil is supplied from a reservoir which is integral with the casing of the integrated drive generator, and is circulated by a charge pump driven by the output shaft of the hydraulic transmission system. The oil is passed through an oil cooler mounted on the engine, and, depending on the installation, the cooling medium for the oil may either be air tapped from a low-pressure stage of the compressor or fuel from the fuel system of the aircraft.

The constant speed drive unit is a hydro/mechanical device, and as has been previously stated, the oil for the integrated drive unit is contained in a reservoir which is built into the generator assembly. The C.S.U. is controlled by a governor assembly which is an integral part of the C.S.U. The output from the generator passes through a Frequency Controller which monitors the frequency of the generator output. Any variation in frequency output beyond set limits causes the frequency controller to send signals to the C.S.U. governor which in turn corrects the frequency output.

A frequency meter is also provided to permit the pilot to monitor the generator frequency in the cockpit. In systems which have more than one generator, only one frequency meter is fitted in the cockpit with a mode selector to select the generator frequency reading required.

There are two warning lights fitted to the C.S.U. The first will illuminate in the event there is excessive temperature within the C.S.U., the other light illuminates should the oil pressure drop below a certain value. Should either, or both of these lights illuminate indicating a malfunction within the C.S.U. a manually operated disconnect switch must be operated by the pilot. This will disconnect the C.S.U. drive and can only be re-set on the ground.

When two such A.C. generators are paralleled or load shared, the Active load sharing is borne by the frequency controllers, and the Reactive load sharing is borne by the Voltage regulators. The reactive load on a generator is measured in kVAR, kilovolts ampere reactance. On some generators kVAR meters are fitted in the field circuit.

7.4 Brushless Alternator

One generator now in use is the brushless type. It is more efficient because there are no brushes to wear down or to arc at high altitudes.

This generator consists of a pilot exciter, an exciter, and the main generator system. The necessity for brushes has been eliminated by utilising an integral exciter with a rotating armature that has its A.C. output rectified for the main A.C field, which is also of the rotating type. A brushless alternator is illustrated in Figure 5.

The pilot exciter is an 8-pole, 8,000 r.p.m., 533 c.p.s., A.C. generator. The pilot exciter field is mounted on the main generator rotor shaft and is connected in series with the main generator field (Figure 5). The pilot exciter armature is mounted on the main generator stator. The A.C. output of the pilot exciter is supplied to the voltage regulator, where it is rectified and controlled, and is then impressed on the exciter field winding to furnish excitation for the generator.

The exciter is a small A.C. generator with its field mounted on the main generator stator and its 3-phase armature mounted on the generator rotor shaft. Included in the exciter field are permanent magnets mounted on the main generator stator between the exciter poles.

The exciter field resistance is temperature compensated by a thermistor. This aids regulation by keeping a nearly constant resistance at the regulator output terminals. The exciter output is rectified and impressed on the main generator field and the pilot exciter field. The exciter stator has a stabilising field, which is used to improve stability and to prevent voltage regulator over-corrections for changes in generator output voltage.

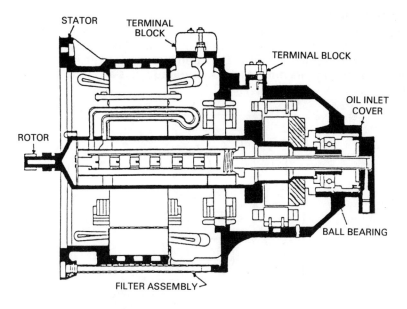

Fig.7-5. A typical brushless alternator.

The A.C. generator shown in Figure 5 is a 6-pole, 8,000 r.p.m. unit having a rating of 31.5 kilovolt amperes (KVA), 115/200 volts, 400 c.p.s. This generator is 3-phase, 4-wire, wye-connected with grounded neutrals. By using an integral A.C. exciter the necessity for brushes within the generator has been eliminated. The A.C. output of the rotating exciter armature is fed directly into the 3-phase, full-wave, rectifier bridge located inside the rotor shaft, which uses high-temperature silicon rectifiers. The D.C. output from the rectifier bridge is fed to the main A.C. generator rotating field.

Voltage regulation is accomplished by varying the strength of the A.C.

exciter stationary fields. Polarity reversals of the A.C. generator are eliminated and radio noise is minimised by the absence of the brushes. Any existing radio noise is further reduced by a noise filter mounted on the alternator.

The rotating pole structure of the generator is laminated from steel punchings, containing all six poles and a connecting hub section. This provides optimum magnetic and mechanical properties.

Some alternators are cooled by circulating oil through steel tubes. The oil used for cooling is supplied from the constant-speed drive assembly. Oil flow between the constant-speed drive and the generator is made possible by ports located in the flange connecting the generator and drive assemblies.

Voltage is built up by using permanent magnet interpoles in the exciter stator. The permanent magnets assure a voltage build up, precluding the necessity of field flashing. The rotor of the alternator may be removed without causing loss of the alternator's residual magnetism.

7.5 Alternator-Rectifier Unit

A type of alternator used in the electrical system of many aircraft weighing less than 5700 kg is show in Figure 7-6. This type of power source is sometimes called a D.C. generator, since it is used in D.C. systems. Although its output is a D.C. voltage, it is an alternator-rectifier unit.

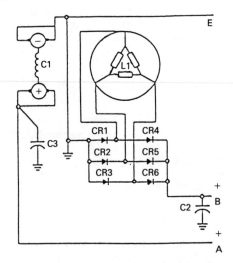

Fig.7-6. Wiring diagram of alternator-rectifier unit.

This type of alternator-rectifier is a self-excited unit but does not contain a permanent magnet. The excitation for starting is obtained from the battery, and immediately after starting, the unit is self-exciting. Cooling air for the alternator is conducted into the unit by a blast air tube on the air inlet cover.

The alternator is directly coupled to the aircraft engine by means of a flexible drive coupling. The D.C. output voltage may be regulated by a carbon pile voltage regulator. The output of the alternator portion of the unit is three-phase alternating current, derived from a three-phase, delta-connected system incorporating a three-phase full-wave bridge rectifier (Figure 7-7).

This unit operates in a speed range from 2,100 to 9,000 r.p.m., with a D.C. output voltage of 26–29 volts and 125 amperes.

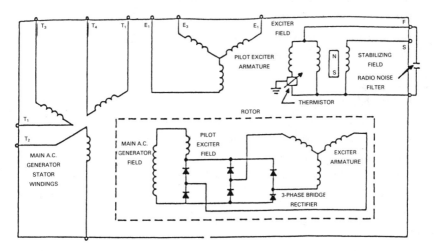

Fig.7-7. Three phase, full wave bridge rectifier.

7.6 Combined A.C. and D.C. Electrical Systems

Many aircraft, especially aircraft of more than 5700 kg employ both a D.C. and an A.C. electrical system. Often the D.C. system is the basic electrical system and consists of paralleled D.C. generators with output of, for example, 300 amperes each.

The A.C. system on such aircraft may include both a fixed frequency and a variable frequency system. The fixed frequency system may consist of three or four inverters and associated controls, protective, and indicating components to provide single-phase, A.C. power for frequency sensitive A.C. equipment. The variable frequency system may consist of two or more engine-driven alternators, with associated control, protective, and indicating components, to provide three-phase, A.C. power for such purposes as resistive heating on propellers, engine ducts and windshields.

Such combined D.C. and A.C. electrical systems normally include an auxiliary source of D.C. power to back up the main system. This generator is often driven by a separate gasoline or turbine-powered unit.

CHAPTER 7
TEST YOURSELF QUESTIONS

A.C. GENERATORS

1. A frequently wild generator:
    (a) is always used as a D.C. generator.
    (b) produces constant frequency but at a variable r.p.m.
    (c) maintains constant r.p.m. but has a variable frequency.
    (d) has a variable frequency output.
    Ref. Ch.7. Para.7.2.

2. In order to load share:
    (a) constant speed generators are normally used.
    (b) constant speed frequency wild generators are used.
    (c) any type of generator may be used.
    (d) frequency wild generators with T.R.U.s may be used.
    Ref. Ch.7. Para.7.3.

3. The constant speed unit of a constant speed generator is controlled by:
    (a) a governor unit.
    (b) a centrifugal clutch mechanism.
    (c) a disconnect switching device.
    (d) a hydraulic pump.
    Ref. Ch.7. Para.7.3.

4. Oil for the operation of the C.S.U. of a constant speed generator is supplied:
    (a) by the engine lubrication system.
    (b) by a self contained system within the generator.
    (c) by the aircraft hydraulic system.
    (d) by the gearbox drive system.
    Ref. Ch.7. Para.7.3.

5. Constant speed A.C. generators are normally:
    (a) self exciting.
    (b) excited by the battery busbar.
    (c) excited by the D.C. supply.
    (d) excited by a separate frequency wild generator.
    Ref. Ch.7. Para.7.3.

8

CONTROL AND REGULATION OF A.C. GENERATORS

8.1 Introduction

Alternators are classified in several ways in order to distinguish properly the various types. One means of classification is by the type of excitation system used. In alternators used on aircraft, excitation can be affected by one of the following methods:

(a) A direct-connected, direct-current generator. This system consists of a D.C. generator fixed on the same shaft with the A.C. generator. A variation of this system is a type of alternator which uses D.C. from the battery for excitation, after which the alternator is self-excited.

(b) By transformation and rectification from the A.C. system. This method depends on residual magnetism for initial A.C. voltage buildup, after which the field is supplied with rectified voltage from the A.C. generator.

(c) Integrated brushless type. This arrangement has a direct-current generator on the same shaft with an alternating-current generator. The excitation circuit is completed through silicon rectifiers rather than a commutator and brushes. The rectifiers are mounted on the generator shaft and their output is fed directly to the alternating-current generator's main rotating field.

Another method of classification is by the number of phases of output voltage. Alterating-current generators may be single-phase, two-phase, three-phase, or even six-phase and more. In the electrical system of aircraft, the three-phase alternator is by far the most common.

Still another means of classification is by the type of stator and rotor used. From this standpoint, there are two types of alternators: the revolving-armature type and the revolving-field type. The revolving-armature alternator is similar in construction to the D.C. generator, in that the armature rotates through a stationary magnetic field. The revolving-armature alternator is found only in alternators of low power rating and generally is not used. In the D.C. generator, the e.m.f. generated in the armature windings is converted into a uni-directional voltage (D.C.) by means of the commutator. In the revolving-armature type of alternator, the generated D.C. voltage is applied unchanged to the load by means of slip rings and brushes.

The revolving-field type of alternator (Figure 8-1) has a stationary armature winding (stator) and a rotating-field winding (rotor). The advantage of having a stationary armature winding is that the armature can be connected directly to the load without having sliding contacts in the load circuit. A rotating armature would require slip rings and brushes to conduct the load current from the armature to the external circuit. Slip rings have a relatively short service life and arc-over is a continual hazard; therefore, high-voltage alternators are usually of the stationary-armature, rotating-field type. The voltage and current supplied to the rotating field are relatively small, and slip rings and brushes for this circuit are adequate. The direct connection to the armature circuit makes possible the use of large cross-section conductors, adequately insulated for high voltage.

Since the rotating-field alternator is used almost universally in aircraft systems, this type will be explained in detail, as a single-phase, two-phase, and three-phase alternator.

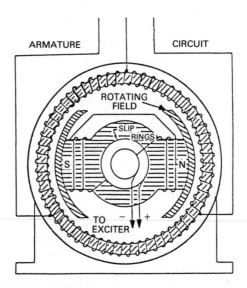

Fig.8-1. Alternator with stationary armature and rotating field.

8.2 Single-Phase Alternator

Since the e.m.f. induced in the armature of a generator is alternating, the same sort of winding can be used on an alternator as on a D.C. generator. This type of alternator is known as a single-phase alternator, but since the power delivered by a single-phase circuit is pulsating, this type of circuit is objectionable in many applications.

A single-phase alternator has a stator made up of a number of windings in series, forming a single circuit in which an output voltage is generated. Figure 8-2 illustrates a schematic diagram of a single-phase alternator having four poles. The stator has four polar groups evenly spaced around the stator frame. The rotor has four poles, with adjacent poles of opposite polarity. As the rotor revolves, A.C. voltages are induced in the stator windings. Since one rotor pole is in the same position relative to a stator winding as any other rotor pole, all stator polar groups are cut by equal numbers of magnetic lines of force at any time. As a result, the voltages induced in all the windings have the same amplitude, or value, at any given instant. The four stator windings are connected to each other so that the A.C. voltages are in phase, or 'series adding'. Assume that rotor pole 1, a south pole, induces a voltage in the direction indicated by the arrow in stator winding 1. Since rotor pole 2 is a north pole, it will induce a voltage in the opposite direction in stator coil 2, with respect to that in coil 1.

For the two induced voltages to be in series addition, the two coils are connected as shown in the diagram. Applying the same reasoning, the voltage induced in stator coil 3 (clockwise rotation of the field) is the same direction (counterclockwise) as the voltage induced in coil 1. Similarly, the direction of the voltage induced in winding 4 is opposite to the direction of the voltage induced in coil 1. All four stator coil groups are connected in series so that the voltages induced in each winding add to give a total voltage that is four times the voltage in any one winding.

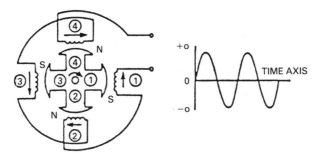

Fig.8-2. Single-phase alternator.

8.3   Two-Phase Alternator

Two-phase alternators have two or more single-phase windings spaced symmetrically around the stator. In a two-phase alternator there are two single-phase windings spaced physically so that the A.C. voltage induced in one is 90° out of phase with the voltage induced in the other. The windings are electrically separate from each other. When one winding is being cut by maximum flux, the other is being cut by no flux. This condition establishes a 90° relation between the two phases.

8.4   Three-Phase Alternator

A three-phase, or polyphase circuit, is used in most aircraft alternators, instead of a single or two-phase alternator. The three-phase alternator has three single-phase windings spaced so that the voltage induced in each winding is 120° out of phase with the voltages in the other two windings. A schematic diagram of a three-phase stator showing all the coils becomes complex and difficult to see what is actually happening.

A simplified schematic diagram, showing each of three phases, is illustrated in Figure 3. The rotor is omitted for simplicity. The waveforms of voltage are shown to the right of the schematic. The three voltages are 120° apart and are similar to the voltages which would be generated by three single-phase alternators whose voltages are out of phase by angles of 120°. The three phases are independent of each other.

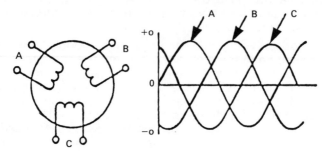

Fig.8-3. Simplified schematic of three-phase alternator with output waveforms.

Rather than have six leads from the three-phase alternator, one of the leads from each phase may be connected to form a common junction. The stator is then called star-connected. The common lead may or may not be brought out of the alternator. If it is brought out, it is called the neutral lead. The simplified schematic (A of Figure 4) shows a star-connected stator with the common lead not brought out. Each load is connected across two phases in series. Thus, R_{AB} is connected across phases A and B in series; R_{AC} is connected across phases A and C in series; and R_{BC} is connected across phases B and C in series.

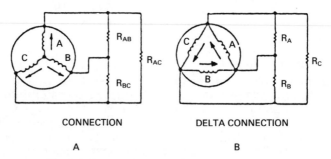

CONNECTION   DELTA CONNECTION

A   B

Fig.8-4. Star and delta-connected alternators.

Therefore, the voltage across each load is larger than the voltage across a single phase. The total voltage, or line voltage, across any two phases is the vector sum of the individual phase voltages. For balanced conditions, the line voltage is 1.73 times the phase voltage. Since there is only one path for current in a line wire and the phase to which it is connected, the line current is equal to the phase current.

A three phase stator can also be connected so that the phases are connected end-to-end as shown in (b) of Fig.8-4. This arrangement is called a delta connection. In delta connection, the voltages are equal to the phase voltages; the line currents are equal to the vector sum of the phase currents, and the line current is equal to 1.73 times the phase current when the loads are balanced.

For equal loads (equal Kw output), the delta connection supplies increased line current at a value of line voltage equal to phase voltage, and the star connection supplies increased line voltage at a value of line current equal to phase current.

8.5 Load-Sharing or Paralleling of A.C. Generators

(a) Frequency-Wild Systems

In systems of this type, the A.C. output is supplied to independent consumer equipment and since the frequency is allowed to go uncontrolled, then paralleling or sharing of the A.C. load is not possible. In most applications this is by design; for example, in electrical de-icing equipment utilising resistance type heaters, a variable frequency has no effect on system operation; therefore reliance is placed more on generator dependability and on the simplicity of the generating system. In rectified A.C. systems frequency is also uncontrolled, but as most of the output is utilised for supplying D.C. consumer equipment, load sharing is more easily accomplished by paralleling the rectified output through equalising circuits in a similar manner to that adopted for D.C. generating systems.

(b) Constant-Frequency Systems

These systems are designed for operation under load-sharing or paralleling conditions and in this connection regulation of the two parameters, real load and reactive load, is required. Real load is the actual working load output in kilowatts (kW) available for supplying the various electrical services, and the reactive load is the so-called 'wattless load' which is in fact the vector sum of the inductive and capacitive currents and voltage in the system expressed in kilovolt-amperes reactive (kVAR).

Since the real load is directly related to the input power from the prime mover, i.e. The aircraft engine, real load-sharing control must be on the engine. There are, however, certain practical difficulties involved, but as it is possible to reference back any real load unbalance to the constant-speed drive unit between engine and generator, real load-sharing control is effected at this unit by adjusting torque at the output drive shaft.

Reactive load unbalances are corrected by controlling the exciter field current delivered by the voltage regulators to their respective generators, in accordance with signals from a reactive load-sharing circuit.

8.6 Voltage Regulation of Alternators

The problem of voltage regulation in an A.C. system does not differ basically from that in a D.C. system. In each case the function of the regulator system is to control voltage, maintain a balance of circulating current throughout the system and eliminate sudden changes in voltage (anti-hunting) when a load is applied to the system. However, there is one important difference between the regulator system of D.C. generators and alternators operated in a parallel configuration. The load carried by any particular D.C. generator in either a two- or four-generator system depends on its voltage as compared with the bus voltage, while the division of load between alternators depends upon the adjustments of their speed governors, which are controlled by the frequency and droop circuits.

When A.C. generators are operated in parallel, frequency and voltage must both be equal. Where a synchronising force is required to equalise only the voltage between D.C. generators, synchronising forces are required to equalise both voltage and speed (frequency) between A.C. generators. On a comparative basis, the synchronising forces for A.C. generators are much greater than for D.C. generators. When A.C. generators are of sufficient size and are operating at unequal frequencies and terminal voltages, serious damage may result if they are suddenly connected to each other through a common bus. To avoid this, the generators must be synchronised as closely as possible before connecting them together.

The output voltage of an alternator is best controlled by regulating the voltage output of the D.C. exciter, which supplies current to the alternator rotor field. This is accomplished as shown in Figure 5 by a carbon-pile regulator of a 28-volt system connected in the field circuit of the exciter. The carbon-pile regulator controls the exciter field current and thus regulates the exciter output voltage applied to the alternator field. The only difference between the D.C. system and the A.C. system is that the voltage coil receives its voltage from the alternator line instead of the D.C. generator. In this arrangement, a three-phase step-down transformer connected to the alternator voltage supplies power to a three-phase, full-wave rectifier. The 28-volt, D.C. output of the rectifier is then applied to the voltage coil of the carbon-pile regulator. Changes in alternator voltage are transferred through the transformer rectifier unit to the voltage coil of the regulator and vary the pressure on the carbon disks. This controls the exciter field current and the exciter output voltage. The exciter voltage anti-hunting or damping transformer is similar to those in D.C. systems and performs the same functions.

The alternator equalising circuit is similar to that of the D.C. system in that the regulator is affected when the circulating current supplied by one alternator differs from that supplied by the others.

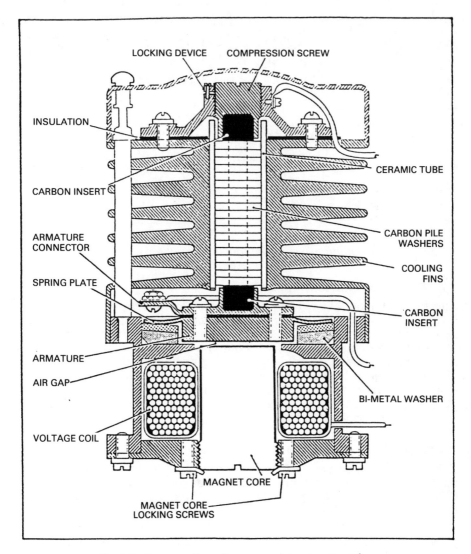

Fig.8-5. Carbon-pile voltage regulator construction.

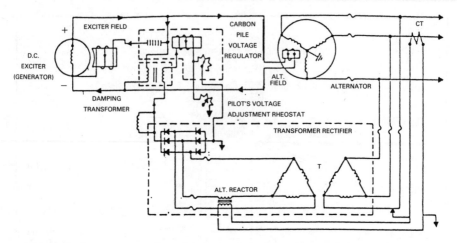

Fig.8-6. Carbon-pile voltage regulator circuit for an alternator.

8.7 Alternator Constant-Speed Drive

Alternators are not always connected directly to the airplane engine like D.C. generators. Since the various electrical devices operating on A.C. supplied by alternators are designed to operate at a certain voltage and at a specified frequency, the speed of the alternators must be constant; however, the speed of an airplane engine varies. Therefore, some alternators are driven by the engine through a constant-speed drive installed between the engine and the alternator. The following discussion of a constant-speed drive system will be based on such a drive, found on large multi-engined aircraft.

The constant-speed drive is a hydraulic transmission which may be controlled either electrically or mechanically.

The constant-speed drive assembly is designed to deliver an output of 6,000 r.p.m., provided the input remains between 2,800 and 9,000 r.p.m. If the input, which is determined by engine speed, is below 6,000 r.p.m., the drive increases the speed in order to furnish the desired output. This stepping up of speed is known as overdrive.

In overdrive, an automobile engine will operate at about the same r.p.m. at 60 m.p.h. as it does in conventional drive at 49 m.p.h. In aircraft, this principle is applied in the same manner. The constant-speed drive enables the alternator to produce the same frequency at slightly above engine-idle r.p.m. as it would at takeoff or cruising r.p.m.

CHAPTER 8
TEST YOURSELF QUESTIONS

CONTROL AND REGULATION OF A.C. GENERATORS

1. In a three phase generator, or alternator, the phases are:
    (a) spaced 90 degrees apart.
    (b) spaced at 45 degree intervals.
    (c) spaced 120 degrees apart.
    (d) may be spaced at any interval provided they are insulated from each other.

    Ref. Ch.8. Para.8.4.

2. In a three phase star connected generator:
    (a) phase current is greater than line current.
    (b) line current is equal to phase current.
    (c) line voltage is equal to phase voltage.
    (d) line voltage is less than phase voltage.

    Ref. Ch.8. Para.8.4.

3. In a star connected three phase generator, if one phase becomes disconnected:
    (a) only that phase will be effected.
    (b) the current on the neutral will remain constant.
    (c) all three phases will be effected.
    (d) the generator will immediately stop.

    Ref. Ch.8. Para.8.4.

4. In a star connected three phase generator, if one phase becomes disconnected:
    (a) line voltage will increase.
    (b) the generator will stop.
    (c) voltage on the neutral will remain constant.
    (d) a large voltage will be thrown on the neutral.

    Ref. Ch.8. Para.8.4.

5. In a delta connected three phase generator:
    (a) line voltage is greater than phase voltage.
    (b) phase current is equal to line current.
    (c) phase voltage is equal to line voltage.
    (d) line voltage is less then phase voltage.

    Ref. Ch.8. Para.8.4.

9

A.C. MOTORS AND CONVERSION EQUIPMENT

9.1 A.C. Motors

Because of its advantages, many types of aircraft motor are designed to operate on alternating current. In general, A.C. motors are less expensive than comparable D.C. motors. In many instances, A.C. motors do not use brushes and commutators and, therefore, sparking at the brushes is avoided. They are very reliable and very little maintenance is needed. Also, they are well suited for constant-speed applications and certain types are manufactured that have, within limits, variable-speed characteristics. Alternating-current motors are designed to operate on poly-phase or single-phase lines and at several voltage ratings.

The subject of A.C. motors is very extensive, and no attempt has been made to cover the entire field. Only the types of A.C. motors most common to aircraft systems are discussed in detail.

The speed of rotation of an A.C. motor depends upon the number of poles and the frequency of the electrical source of power:

$$\text{r.p.m.} = \frac{120 \times \text{Frequency}}{\text{Number of Poles}}$$

Since airplane electrical systems typically operate at 400 cycles, an electric motor at this frequency operates at about seven times the speed of a 60-cycle commercial motor with the same number of poles. Because of this high speed of rotation, 400-cycle A.C. motors are suitable for operating small high-speed rotors, through reduction gears, in lifting and moving heavy loads, such as the wing flaps, the retractable landing gear, and the starting of engines. The 400-cycle induction type motor operates at speeds ranging from 6,000 r.p.m. to 24,000 r.p.m.

Alternating-current motors are rated in horse-power output, operating voltage, full load current, speed, number of phases, and frequency. Whether the motors operate continuously or intermittently (for short intervals) is also considered in the rating.

9.2 Types of A.C. Motors

There are two general types of A.C. motors used in aircraft systems: induction motors and synchronous motors. Either type may be single-phase, two-phase or three-phase.

Three-phase induction motors are used where large amounts of power are required. They operate such devices as starters, flaps, landing gears, and hydraulic pumps.

Single-phase induction motors are used to operate devices such as surface locks, intercooler shutters, and oil shutoff valves in which the power requirement is low.

Three-phase synchronous motors operate at constant synchronous speeds and are commonly used to operate flux gate compasses and propeller synchroniser systems.

Single-phase synchronous motors are common sources of power to operate electric clocks and other small precision equipment. They require some auxiliary method to bring them up to synchronous speeds; that is to start them. Usually the starting winding consists of an auxiliary stator winding.

9.3   Three-Phase Induction Motor

The three-phase A.C. induction motor is also called a squirrel-cage motor. Both single-phase and three-phase motors operate on the principle of a rotating magnetic field. A horseshoe magnet held over a compass needle is a simple illustration of the principle of the rotating field. The needle will take a position parallel to the magnetic flux passing between the two poles of the magnet. If the magnet is rotated, the compass needle will follow. A rotating magnetic field can be produced by a two- or three-phase current flowing through two or more groups of coils wound on inwardly projecting poles of an iron frame. The coils on each group of poles are wound alternately in opposite directions to produce opposite polarity, and each group is connected to a separate phase of voltage. The operating principle depends on a revolving, or rotating, magnetic field to produce torque. The key to understanding the induction motor is a thorough understanding of the rotating magnetic field.

9.4   Rotating Magnetic Field

The field structure shown in A in Figure 9-1 has poles whose windings are energised by three A.C. voltages, a, b and c. These voltages have equal magnitude but differ in phase, as shown in B of Figure 9-1.

At the instant of time shown as 0 in B of Figure 9-1 the resultant magnetic field produced by the application of the three voltages has its greatest intensity in a direction extending from pole 1 to pole 4. Under this condition, pole 1 can be considered as a north pole and pole 4 as a south pole.

At the instant of time shown as 1, the resultant magnetic field will have its greatest intensity in the direction extending from pole 2 to pole 5; in this case, pole 2 can be considered as a north pole and pole 5 as a south pole. Thus, between instant 0 and instant 1, the magnetic field has rotated clockwise.

At instant 2, the resultant magnetic field has its greatest intensity in the direction from pole 3 to pole 6, and the resultant magnetic field has continued to rotate clockwise.

At instant 3, poles 4 and 1 can be considered as north and south poles,

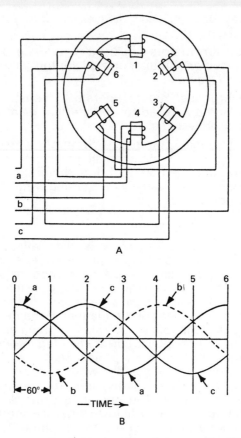

Fig.9-1. Rotating magnetic field developed by application of three-phase voltages.

respectively, and the field has rotated still further.

At later instants of time, the resultant magnetic field rotates to other positions while travelling in a clockwise direction, a single revolution of the field occurring in one cycle. If the exciting voltages have a frequency of 60 c.p.s., the magnetic field makes 60 revolutions per second, or 3,600 r.p.m. This speed is known as the synchronous speed of the rotating field.

9.5 Rotary Converting Equipment

The most commonly used item to be included under this heading is the machine which converts D.C. into A.C. and is variously called a 'rotary converter', 'motor-generator' and an 'inverter'. All three terms can, understandably, cause some confusion regarding their definition, with the result that they tend to be loosely applied to machines which, although performing the same function, have quite different constructional and electrical circuit features. It is not the intention here to justify terminology and applications but the following details may serve to clarify the position.

Rotary Converter

This is, by definition, a 'synchronous machine with a single armature winding having a commutator and slip rings for converting A.C. into D.C. or vice versa'. These machines are not used in aircraft and where the term 'rotary converter' is applied reference to an inverter is more often then not intended.

Motor-generators

These are a 'combination of one or more generators directly coupled to one or more generators directly coupled to one or more motors'. Thus a unit essentially comprises two electrically separate machines mechanically coupled. A D.C. to A.C. type of unit is employed in one or two types of aircraft for the supply of secondary A.C. power, and in such an application is sometimes referred to as a motor alternator and also as an 'inverter'.

Inverter

This term is generally accepted as referring to a D.C. to A.C. type of rotary converter having separate D.C. armature and A.C. rotor windings, located in the same slots and sharing the same field system. The A.C. output is derived from the rotor via slip rings.

An inverter is used in some aircraft systems to convert a portion of the aircraft's D.C. power to A.C. This A.C. is used mainly for instruments, radio, radar, lighting and other accessories. These inverters are usually built to supply current at a frequency of 400 c.p.s., but some are designed to provide more than one voltage; for example, 26-volt A.C. in one winding and 115 volts in another.

There are two basic types of inverters: the rotary and the static. Either type can be single-phase or multiphase. The multiphase inverter is lighter for the same power rating than the single-phase, but there are complications in distributing multiphase power and in keeping the loads balanced.

9.6 Rotary Inverters

There are many sizes, types and configurations of rotary inverters. Such inverters are essentially A.C. generators and D.C. motors in one housing. The generator field, or armature, and the motor field, or armature, are mounted on a common shaft which will rotate within the housing. One common type of rotary inverter is the permanent magnet inverter.

9.7 Static Conversion Equipment

Transformers

A transformer is a device for converting A.C. at one frequency and voltage to A.C. at the same frequency but at another voltage. It consists of three main parts: (i) an iron core which provides a circuit of low reluctance for an alternating magnetic field created by, (ii) a primary winding which is connected to the main power source and (iii) a secondary winding which receives electrical energy by mutual induction from the primary winding and delivers it to the secondary circuit. There are two classes of transformers, voltage or power transformers and current transformers.

Principle

The three main parts are shown schematically in Figure 2. When an alternating voltage is applied to the primary winding an alternating current will flow and by self-induction will establish a voltage in the primary winding which is opposite and almost equal to the applied voltage. The difference between these two voltages will allow just enough current (excitation current) to flow in the primary winding to set up an alternating magnetic flux in the core. The flux cuts across the secondary winding and by mutual induction (in practice both windings are wound one on the other) a voltage is established in the secondary winding.

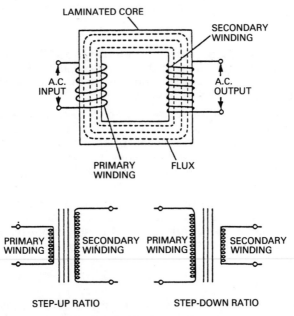

Fig.9-2. Transformer Principle.

When a load is connected to the secondary winding terminals, the secondary voltage causes current to flow through the winding and a magnetic flux is produced which tends to neutralise the magnetic flux produced by the primary current. This, in turn, reduces the self-induced, or opposition, voltage in the primary winding, and allows more current to flow in it to restore the core flux to a value which is only very slightly less than the no-load value.

The primary current increases as the secondary load current increases, and decreases as the secondary load current decreases. When the load is disconnected, the primary winding current is again reduced to the small excitation current sufficient only to magnetise the core.

To accomplish the function of changing voltage from one value to another, one winding is wound with more turns than the other. For example, if the primary winding has 200 turns and the secondary 1000 turns, the voltage available at the secondary terminals will be $\frac{1000}{200}$, or 5 times as great as the voltage applied to the primary winding. This ratio of turns (N_2) in the secondary to the number of turns (N_1) in the primary is called the turns or transformation ratio (r) and it is expressed by the equation

$$r = \frac{N_2}{N_1} = \frac{E_2}{E_1}$$

where E_1 and E_2 are the respective voltages of the two windings.

When the transformation ratio is such that the transformer delivers a higher secondary voltage than the primary voltage it is said to be of the 'step-up' type. Conversely, a 'step-down' transformer is one which lowers the secondary voltage. The circuit arrangements for both types are also shown in Figure 2.

9.8 Auto-Transformers

In circuit applications normally requiring only a small step-up or step-down of voltage, a special variant of transformer design is employed and this is known as an auto-transformer. Its circuit arrangement is shown in Figure 3 and from this it will be noted that its most notable feature is that it consists of a single winding tapped to form primary and secondary parts. In the example illustrated the tappings provide a stepped-up voltage output, since the number of primary turns is less than that of the secondary turns.

When a voltage is applied to the primary terminals current will flow through the portion of the winding spanned by these terminals. The magnetic flux due to this current will flow through the core and will therefore, link with the whole of the winding. Those turns between the primary terminals act in the same way as the primary winding of a conventional transformer, and so they produce a self-induction voltage

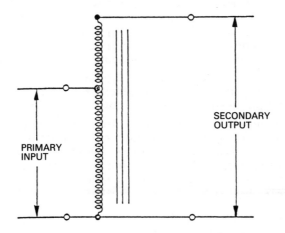

Fig.9-3. Circuit arrangements of an auto-transformer.

in opposition to the applied voltage. The voltage induced in the remaining turns of the winding will be additive, thereby giving a secondary output voltage greater than the applied voltage. When a load circuit is connected to the secondary terminals, a current due to the induced voltage will flow through the whole winding and will be in opposition to the primary current from the input terminals. Since the turns between the primary terminals are common to input and output circuits alike they carry the difference between the induced current and primary current, and they may therefore be wound with smaller gauge wire than the remainder of the winding. Auto-transformers may also be designed for use in consumer circuits requiring three-phase voltage at varying levels.

9.9 Transformer-Rectifier Units

Transformer-rectifier units (T.R.U.'s) are combinations of static transformers and rectifiers, and are utilised in some A.C. systems as secondary supply units, and also as the main conversion units in aircraft having rectified A.C. power systems.

9.10 Static Inverters

In many applications where continuous D.C. voltage must be converted to alternating voltage, static inverters are used in place of rotary inverters or motor generator sets. The rapid progress being made by the semiconductor industry is extending the range of applications of such equipment into voltage and power ranges which would have been impractical a few years ago. Some such applications are power supplies for frequency-sensitive military and commercial A.C. equipment, aircraft emergency A.C. systems, and conversion of wide frequency range power to precise frequency power.

The use of static inverters in small aircraft also has increased rapidly in the last few years, and the technology has advanced to the point that static inverters are available for any requirement filled by rotary inverters. For example, 250 VA emergency A.C. supplies operated from aircraft batteries are in production, as are 2,500 VA main A.C. supplies operated from a varying frequency generator supply. This type of equipment has certain advantages for aircraft applications, particularly the absence of moving parts and the adaptability to conduction cooling.

Static inverters, referred to as solid-state inverters, are manufactured in a wide range of types and models, which can be classified by the shape of the A.C. output waveform and the power output capabilities.

Since static inverters use solid-state components, they are considerably smaller, more compact and much lighter in weight than rotary inverters. Depending on the output power rating required, static inverters that are no longer than a typical airspeed indicator can be used in aircraft systems. Some of the features of static inverters are:

1 High efficiency.
2 Low maintenance, long life.
3 No warm up period required.
4 Capable of starting under load.

5   Extremely quiet operation.

6   Fast response to load changes.

Static inverters are commonly used to provide power for such frequency-sensitive instruments as the attitude gyro and directional gyro. They also provide power for autosyn and magnesyn indicators and transmitters, rate gyros, radar and other airborne applications.

9.11   Magnetic Amplifiers

The magnetic amplifier is a control device being employed at an increasing rate in many aircraft electrical and electronic systems. This is because of its ruggedness, stability, and safety in comparison to vacuum tubes.

The principles on which the magnetic amplifier operates can best be explained by reviewing the operation of a simple transformer. If an A.C. voltage is applied to the primary of an iron core transformer, the iron core will be magnetised and demagnetised at the same frequency as that of the applied voltage. This, in turn, will induce a voltage in the transformer secondary. The output voltage across the terminals of the secondary will depend on the relationship of the number of turns in the primary and the secondary of the transformer.

The iron core of the transformer has a saturation point after which the application of a greater magnetic force will produce no change in the intensity of magnetisation. Hence, there will be no change in transformer output, even if the input is greatly increased.

The magnetic amplifier circuit in Figure 9-4 will be used to explain how a simple magnetic amplifier functions. Assume that there is 1 ampere of current in coil A, which has 10 turns of wire. If coil B has 10 turns of wire, an output of 1 ampere will be obtained if coil B is properly loaded. By applying direct current to coil C, the core of the magnetic amplifier coil can be further magnetised. Assume that coil C has the proper number of turns and, upon the application of 30 milliamperes, that the core is magnetised to the point where 1 ampere on coil A results in only 0.24 amperes output from coil B.

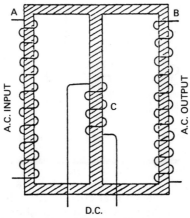

Fig.9-4. Magnetic amplifier circuit.

By making the D.C. input to coil C continuously variable from 0 to 30 milliamperes and maintaining an input of 1 ampere on coil A, it is possible to control the output of coil B to any point between 0.24 amperes and 1 ampere in this example. The term 'amplifier' is used for this arrangement because, by use of a few milliamperes, control of an output of 1 or more amperes is obtained.

The same procedure can be used with the circuit shown in Figure 9-5.

By controlling the extent of magnetisation of the iron ring, it is possible to control the amount of current flowing to the load, since the amount of magnetisation controls the impedance of the A.C. input winding. This type of magnetic amplifier is called a simple saturable reactor circuit.

Adding a rectifier to such a circuit would remove half the cycle of the A.C. input and permit a direct current to flow to the load. The amount of D.C. flowing in the load circuit is controlled by a D.C. control winding (sometimes referred to as bias). This type of magnetic amplifier is referred to as being self-saturating.

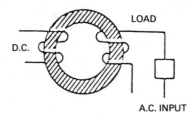

Fig.9-5. Saturable reactor circuit.

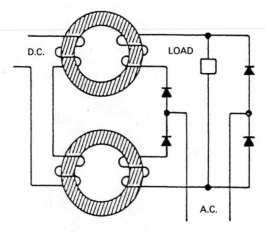

Fig.9-6. Self-saturating, full-wave magnetic amplifier.

In order to use the full A.C. input power, a circuit such as that shown in Figure 9-6 may be used. This circuit uses a full-wave bridge rectifier. The load will receive a controlled direct current by using the full A.C. input. This type of circuit is known as a self-saturating, full-wave magnetic amplifier.

CHAPTER 9
TEST YOURSELF QUESTIONS

A.C. MOTORS AND CONVERSION EQUIPMENT

1. A three phase induction motor is sometimes called a:
   (a) squirrel cage motor.
   (b) stepa motor.
   (c) synchronous motor.
   (d) beta motor.

   Ref. Ch.9. Para.9.3.

2. An inverter is used:
   (a) to convert A.C. to D.C.
   (b) to increase or decrease the speed of an electric motor.
   (c) to convert D.C. to A.C.
   (d) to step up or step down the voltage of an A.C. Generator.

   Ref. Ch.9. Para.9.5.

3. A. T.R.U. may be used:
   (a) in a A.C. circuit to step down, or up, voltage and rectify the current.
   (b) in a D.C. circuit to step up, or step down voltage and rectify the Direct Current.
   (c) in a D.C. circuit to convert D.C. to A.C.
   (d) in an A.C. circuit to produce constant frequency current.

   Ref. Ch.9. Para.9.9.

4. Static inverters may be used to supply:
   (a) frequency wild A.C. from aircraft batteries.
   (b) constant frequency D.C. from aircraft batteries.
   (c) constant frequency A.C. from aircraft batteries.
   (d) frequency wild D.C. from aircraft batteries.

   Ref. Ch.9. Para.9.10.

5. Three Phase induction motors are used:
   (a) to provide small amounts of power to operate clocks etc:
   (b) to operate devices requiring large amounts of power.
   (c) only as inverters.
   (d) as a form of auto transformer.

   Ref. Ch.9. Para.9.3.

10

GENERAL INFORMATION

10.1 General

To prevent problems which arise from brush wear, constant frequency A.C. (C.F.A.C.) generating systems are fitted with rotating rectifier brushless machines. The generator may be self excited under the influence of a rotating magnet pilot exciter or externally excited from the aircraft D.C. bus bar on initial start-up, after which excitation is through monitored generator output.

Generator output is controlled 3 phase 200/115 volt 400 Hz and rated in Kilo-volt Amperes (K.V.A.).

Generator cooling can be by Ram Air, Bleed Air or Oil. Ram air in use after take-off with augmentation of bleed air during flight at low speeds. Bleed air cooling in use on ground. Oil cooling by pressure or spray. Generator temperatures are monitored on main electrical panel. Power output of the generator is indicated by an ammeter.

10.2 Voltage Regulator

The voltage regulator maintains the output voltage of the generator constant irrespective of the load current. This is achieved by continual adjustments to the generator field current.

Two basic types of regulator in use: Variable impedance in the form of a magnetic amplifier used to control the current input to the main generator exciter, pulse control regulation using thyristor or transistors to control the current into the main exciter. A voltmeter on the electrical panel indicates the generator voltage output.

10.3 Frequency Controller

The frequency controller provides small adjustment signals to the C.S.D.U. governor so that the generator output frequency is maintained at 400 Hz. Utilises magnetic amplifier or transistored frequency discriminator circuits, to supply signals to the C.S.D.U. governor.

10.4 Fault Protection Unit

In order to achieve the necessary degree of safety required, a C.F.A.C. generating system must include certain protection circuits to continually monitor system performance. Within the protection unit are transistor logic circuits and controls for the opening or closing of the Generator Control Relay (G.C.R.) and the Generator Control Breaker (G.C.B.) depending on the integrity of the circuit.

In a single channel system protection is provided for:

Over voltage
Under voltage
Generator over speed
Generator under speed
Generator temperature
Line to line bus bar faults
Line to earth bus bar faults.

10.5 Generator Control Relay (G.C.R. switches)

When the generator control relay is closed, the generator field excitation circuit from the voltage regulator is completed. When tripped (open) the generator is de-excited and the generator circuit breaker (G.C.B.) will also trip (open). A signal from the fault protection unit will trip the G.C.R.

10.6 Generator Circuit Breaker (G.C.B.)

Closing a generator circuit breaker connects the generator output to the generator bus bar. Under paralleled conditions the G.C.B. will not close unless voltage, frequency and phase sequence are correct. Closing of the G.C.B. is usually indicated on the control panel by a magnetic in-line indicator or lights. The closure of the G.C.B. bringing a generator 'on line' will automatically disconnect any external power supplies connected.

10.7 Generator Failure Warning Light

A generator failure warning light which comes 'on' when the associated generator circuit breaker (G.C.B.) is tripped; the centralised warning system (C.W.S.) light will show and audio systems will operate.

10.8 System Components (Multi channel)

When more than one source of Constant Frequency Alternating Current is used and the systems are operated in parallel, then other requirements become necessary.

10.9 Bus Tie Breakers (B.T.B.)

A bus tie breaker connects a generator to its synchronising bus bar. Control of a B.T.B. is automatic and in its normal position it is closed, but trips open under fault conditions. Visual indications by means of magnetic line indicators on the control panel, centralised warning systems and audio. If a fault on the generator system causes the G.C.B. to trip the B.T.B. will reset.

10.10 Reactive Load Sharing Control

This is necessary to ensure that once systems are paralleled the reactive load K.V.A.R. on the bus bars is shared equally between systems. Reactive load sharing is carried out by the voltage regulator.

10.11 Active Load Sharing

This is necessary to ensure that once systems are paralleled the real load Kw on the bus bars is shared equally between systems. Active load sharing is carried out by the frequency controller.

Reactive and active load sharing circuits are not made until the generator control breakers and the generator bus tie breakers are closed, i.e. systems are paralleled.

10.12 Protection Devices

When the systems are paralleled, discrimination circuits are required to ensure that only the faulty system is disconnected from the bus bar in event of a generator failure.

Inter connections are made between the individual protective units when the generator control breakers and the bus tie breakers are made, i.e. systems are paralleled.

10.13 Synchronising Unit

Before two generating systems are paralleled the generators must be 'In Phase'. The synchronising unit ensures that the bus tie breaker cannot be closed until the generators are 'In Phase'. Two methods in use:

(a) Manual (Lamp Dark Method)
   A synchronising lamp on the panel will be out or 'dark' when synchronism is achieved. Operation of the Sync push switch, closes the bus tie breaker.

(b) Automatic Control
   The circuit is so designed that the Sync push switch can be pressed but the bus tie breaker will not close until the systems are 'In Phase'.

10.14 Meters Kw/K.V.A.R.

The Kw/K.V.A.R. meters are employed in parallel generating systems to indicate the Kw (Real Power) or K.V.A.R. (Reactive Power) output of the machine. Normally the meters will indicate Kw output until a selector switch is pressed when they will indicate K.V.A.R.

(a) Kw. Real Load
   The real load borne by a generator is the power that is consumed doing useful work, i.e. wattful current.

(b) K.V.A.R. Reactive Load
   The reactive load borne by a generator is the power which is used to produce electro-magnetic fields. As in each half cycle electric power is converted into electro-magnetic fields and back again to electric power, no useful work is accomplished. This is the wattless current component of the load.

10.15 Voltmeters and Frequency Meters

One voltmeter and one frequency meter only is provided for a C.F.A.C. system. Selection of a particular generating system by means of a multi position rotary switch enables the voltage and frequency for the selected generator to be observed.

10.16 Emergency Supplies

Unlike the D.C. system, batteries cannot be used as emergency A.C.

power. Therefore other means have to be supplied. These take the form of small A.C. generator system separate from the primary generation systems driven from either a Ram Air Turbine (R.A.T.) or an Auxiliary Power Unit (A.P.U.), or Static Inverters.

10.17 Ram Air Turbine (R.A.T.)

A 200/115 volt 3 phase ram air driven turbo/generator controlled at a nominal 400 Hz, lowered into the slipstream to ensure that there is an emergency source of A.C. power for the limited operation of flight and radio services in the event of a total main generator failure.

Once lowered into the slipstream retraction can only be carried out on the ground.

10.18 Auxiliary Power Unit (A.P.U.)

A constant speed gas turbine engine, usually mounted in the fuselage tail cone, driving a 200/115 volt 3 phase generator which can be used for ground servicing supplies or emergency supplies in the air. In some aircraft the A.P.U. is on during take off and landing.

10.19 Static Inverter

A transistorised (solid state) device which will provide 115 volts 400 Hz A.C. power for the limited operation of flight and radio services in the event of total electrical power generation failure. It is powered with D.C. from the aircraft battery which, if fully charged, should supply power for approximately 30 minutes.

10.20 Ground Power C.F.A.C. Systems

The standard ground power unit requirement is for a 3 phase 200/115 volt 400 Hz A.C. supply. This supply can be plugged into the aircraft to maintain all electrical services.

A constant frequency aircraft power supply embodies automatic protection circuits which ensure that:

Ground power cannot be connected to the aircraft distribution system if the system is already being supplied from its own generating system.

Ground power cannot be connected if the phase sequence of the supply is incorrect.

Ground power is rejected and switched off at source if over voltage occurs.

10.21 Conclusion

Because of the problems of parallel operation and the higher voltages involved C.F.A.C. generating systems are more complex than D.C. systems. Therefore C.F.A.C. systems are only used on aircraft where the A.C. power requirements are much greater than the D.C. requirements, and hence a D.C. system would be uneconomical to use. C.F.A.C. multi channel systems are often operated as independent non-paralleled systems to reduce system complexity and to increase system safety.

FINAL PRACTICE PAPER

A.C. AND D.C. ELECTRICS

1. The electrical pressure which exists in a conductor is known as:
   (a) the current.
   (b) the resistance.
   (c) the electromotive force.
   (d) the field current.

   Ref. Ch.2. Para.2.3.

2. The unit of potential difference in a circuit is the:
   (a) ohm.
   (b) watt.
   (c) e.m.f.
   (d) volt.

   Ref. Ch.2. Para.2.4.

3. E.M.F. is induced in a conductor:
   (a) as its cuts the lines of magnetic force.
   (b) if it is placed in a magnetic field.
   (c) if the conductor moves parallel to the lines of magnetic force.
   (d) if the conductor has current flowing in it.

   Ref. Ch.3. Para.3.2.

4. The magnitude of an induced E.M.F. is dependent upon:
   (a) the speed of rotation of the generator.
   (b) the strength of the magnetic field.
   (c) the strength of residual magnetism.
   (d) the number of armature laminations.

   Ref. Ch.3. Para.3.4.

5. In a D.C. Generator, sometimes:
   (a) D.C. is converted to A.C. by a commutator.
   (b) D.C. is converted to A.C. by an inverter.
   (c) initial excitation is provided by current from the field circuit.
   (d) commutation supplies D.C. to the bus bar.

   Ref. Ch.3. Para.3.6.

6. The state of charge of a battery must be checked:
   (a) once a year.
   (b) every seven days.

   (c) every three months.
   (d) every six months.

Ref. Ch.4. Para.4.7.

7. The specific gravity of an individual battery cell is checked with:
   (a) a voltmeter.
   (b) an ammeter.
   (c) a specograph.
   (d) a hydrometer.

Ref. Ch.4. Para.4.7.

8. When the battery is connected to the bus bar:
   (a) the battery ammeter will indicate on the + side.
   (b) the cut out switch is open.
   (c) the generator will stop.
   (d) the generator warning light is off.

Ref. Ch.5. Para.5.12.

9. An inertia switch:
   (a) isolates the generator if it excessively overvolts.
   (b) isolates the batteries when the aircraft crashes.
   (c) isolates the generator drive if the aircraft crashes.
   (d) isolates the batteries when the main isolation switch is moved
        to the off position.

Ref. Ch.5. Para.5.14.

10. The failure of a hydraulic system may be indicated by the action of:
   (a) an inertia switch.
   (b) a micro switch.
   (c) a flow switch.
   (d) a pressure switch.

Ref. Ch.5. Para.5.16.

11. Damage to the motor of a linear actuator, in an overload situation, is
    prevented by:
   (a) the electro-magnetic brake, when the coil is energised.
   (b) the electro-magnetic brake when the coil is de-energised.
   (c) the limit switches, when both move to the open position.
   (d) the clutch, which will slip.

Ref. Ch.5. Para.5.28.

12. The strength of a magnetic field around a conductor:
   (a) depends on the current flowing in it.

(b) depends upon the direction of current flow.

(c) depends upon the current in volts and the length of the conductor.

(d) depends upon the current in ohms and the length of the conductor.

Ref. Ch.2. Para.2.10.

13. A battery rated at 12 volts consists of:
    (a) 12 cells in series.
    (b) 6 cells in parallel.
    (c) 6 cells in series.
    (d) 12 cells in parallel.

Ref. Ch.4. Para.4.4.

14. The battery in a D.C. supply system is prevented from discharging into the generator when the battery is connected to the bus bar:
    (a) by the battery switch when open.
    (b) by the cut out switch when open.
    (c) by the voltage coil.
    (d) by the differential switch when it is closed.

Ref. Ch.3. Para.3.24.

15. Initial excitation of a D.C. Generator is achieved through:
    (a) the battery bus bar.
    (b) the field windings.
    (c) residual magnetism from the field circuit.
    (d) residual magnetism from the magnetic poles.

Ref. Ch.3. Para.3.24.

16. When load shedding takes place:
    (a) voltage reduces at the bus bar.
    (b) field current increases.
    (c) current at the bus bar reduces.
    (d) current at the bus bar increases.

Ref. Ch.3. Para.3.24.

17. In a star connected three phase generator:
    (a) phase voltage is less than line voltage.
    (b) line current is greater than phase current.
    (c) phase voltage is greater than line voltage.
    (d) phase voltage is equal to line voltage.

Ref. Ch.8. Para.8.4.

18. Static inverters may be used to supply:
    (a) emergency constant frequency A.C.
    (b) emergency constant frequency D.C.
    (c) emergency frequency wild A.C.
    (d) emergency frequency wild D.C.

                                            Ref. Ch.9. Para.9.10.

19. A pilot excitor is:
    (a) a small separate D.C. generator used to excite the main A.C. generator.
    (b) a small D.C. generator mounted on the same drive shaft as the main A.C. generator.
    (c) a small battery excitor.
    (d) a generator excitor operated by an impulse mechanism.

                                            Ref. Ch.7. Para.7.3.

20. In a star connected A.C. Generator, each load is connected:
    (a) a single phase.
    (b) between two phases
    (c) across all three phases.
    (d) between the phase and neutral.

                                            Ref. Ch.8. Para.8.4.

Note: When making your choice of answer, choose the most correct answer.